TRICKS AND AMUSEMENTS

WITH
COINS, CARDS, STRING, PAPER AND MATCHES

Compiled and Illustrated

by

R. M. Abraham

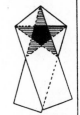

DOVER PUBLICATIONS, INC.
NEW YORK

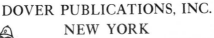

Published in Canada by General Publishing Company, Ltd., 30 Lesmill Road, Don Mills, Toronto,
Ontario.
Published in the United Kingdom by Constable
and Company, Ltd., 10 Orange Street, London WC 2.

This Dover edition was first published in 1964
under the title *Diversions and Pastimes*. It is a
revised edition of the work originally published
under that title by Constable and Company in 1933.

.

International Standard Book Number: 0-486-21127-4
Library of Congress Catalog Card Number: 64-13455

Manufactured in the United States of America
Dover Publications, Inc.
180 Varick Street
New York, N. Y. 10014

" Recreation should sometimes be given to the mind, that it may be restored to you in better condition for thinking."

INTRODUCTION

THE publication of "Winter Nights Entertainments"* in the autumn of 1932 brought a great many letters from readers in all parts of the world. All of these letters were more than kind, and most of them were demands for another book containing " the mixture as before." Some expressed a desire for more of this, or more of that, so, in compiling the present volume an attempt has been made to meet the wishes of the majority. The section on problems has in consequence been enlarged and divided into two parts—easy, and not so easy. It has been more fully illustrated in an endeavour to mitigate that sinking feeling which the very thought of a problem induces in some readers. The section dealing with string games, contains for reference all the knots and bends in general use at sea. Most of the ornamental knots are also described and illustrated. These are very difficult to remember, but anyone with average patience should find it easy to make up, even the most complicated knots with the help of the illustrations. Match, coin, paper and strong-man games have been included, so that everybody may find some simple pastime for those odd blank hours when the only alternative is, to " sit and think," or, as more often happens, " just to sit."

R. M. ABRAHAM.

FITZROY SQUARE, W.I.

CONTENTS

Note on English Currency

1 pound (£) = 20 shillings
1 shilling (s) = 12 pence
1 penny (d) = 4 farthings

EASY PROBLEMS

" Shall quips, and sentences, and these paper bullets of the brain awe a man from the career of his humour."—*Much Ado About Nothing.*

Solutions on p. 111

EASY PROBLEMS

1

THE PORTRAIT

A WOMAN pointing to a portrait of a man said to her father, " that man's mother was my mother's mother-in-law." What relation was the woman to the subject of the portrait ?

2

THE BAG OF FARTHINGS

A shopkeeper had a large number of farthings which he decided to pay into his bank. On the paying-in slip he wrote down the actual number of farthings (it was a five-figure number). The cashier, after a moment's thought, turned this number into £ s. d. by simply inserting two colons. What was the number of farthings paid in ?

3

LARGEST AND SMALLEST SUM

What is the largest sum in pounds, shillings, pence and farthings which can be written down, using the digits 1 to 9 once only ? What is the smallest sum which can be written down under the same conditions ?

4

SMITH'S WIDOW'S SISTER

In the year 1795 a man named Charles Smith married the sister of his widow. How did he do that ?

5

TEN NOUGHTS

Write down ten noughts and the word " trick " thus :

o o o o o o o o o o trick.

Add six strokes to them and make a sentence.

6

SOLDIER AND HIS DOG

With three strokes of a pen draw a picture of a soldier and his dog entering a house.

7

A PARADOXICAL WEDDING

From " The Lady's Magazine," 1782

A wedding there was and a dance there must be,
And who should stand first ?   Thus all did agree,
Old Gransire, and Grandam, should lead the dance down ;
Two fathers, two mothers, should step the same ground ;
Two daughters stood up, and danced with their sires,
(The room was so warm, they wanted no fires)
And also two sons, who danced with their mothers,
Three sisters there were, and danced with three brothers ;
Two uncles vouchsaf'd with nieces to dance ;
With nephews, to jig it, it pleased two aunts ;
Three husbands would dance with none but their wives,
(As bent so to do, the rest of their lives).
The Granddaughter chose the jolly Grandson,
And bride she would dance with bridegroom or none.
A company choice their number to fix,
I told them all o'er, and found them but six
All honest and true, from incest quite free,
Their marriages good ;—pray, how could that be ?

8

PUZZLE PUNCTUATION

Punctuate the following sentence :
Smith where Jones had had had had had had had had had had had the examiners' approval.

9

TWO FRIENDS

Silas P. Sloptootle, the famous financier, was walking across London Bridge, a few steps in front of his friend Sniftkins. Silas was the father of Sniftkins's son. How was that possible?

10

A HECTIC WEEK

When the day after to-morrow is yesterday, to-day will be as far from Sunday as to-day was from Sunday when the day before yester-day was to-morrow. What day is it now?

11

THE FLY AND THE CYCLISTS

A PROBLEM IN CONVERGENT SERIES?

Two cyclists, 20 miles apart, start at the same instant and ride towards each other along a straight road at a speed of 10 miles per hour. At the same instant a fly on the forehead of one of the riders starts to fly at 15 miles per hour towards the other rider, alights on his forehead, and then flies back to the first rider. The fly travels back and forth over the continuously decreasing distance between the two riders until it is finally squashed as the foreheads of the two riders meet. How far has the fly flown when all his journeys are added together?

12

THE RACEHORSE

A trainer owned a very promising trotting pony which he decided to enter for an important race. The stable in which the pony was kept, was in rather an isolated position, in an old mill alongside the railway track. There was a siding from the railway into the mill, and it was the custom to load the horses into trucks which then ran by gravity down an incline to the railway station. As the trainer had no assistant, and had other matters to attend to, he engaged an old man as a night watchman to look after the pony.

When the trainer arrived at the stable in the morning of the day before the race, he found the old man in a very perturbed state. He begged the trainer not to enter for the race, because he had had a dream during the night that he and the trainer had placed the pony in the truck, coasted down to the station, and arrived there just as the express was passing through. They had both been killed and the pony was so badly injured that it had to be shot. The trainer immediately dismissed the old man. Why did he do so?

13

MAN DREAMING IN CHURCH

A man accompanied his wife to Church on a very hot Sunday. During the sermon he became drowsy, his head nodded forward, and he fell into an uneasy sleep. He dreamt that he was a victim of the French Revolution and that he was on the scaffold waiting for the guillotine to descend. His wife turned round and, seeing that he was asleep, gave him a sharp tap on the back of his neck with her fan. He died from the shock without uttering a sound. What is wrong with this story?

14

BOTTLE AND CORK

If a bottle and its cork together cost two and a half cents, and the bottle alone costs two cents more than the cork, what is the cost of the cork?

15

RELATIONS

A mother to her daughter spake
Daughter said she arise,
Thy daughter to her daughter take
Whose daughter's daughter cries.

16

MISSING WORDS

Fill in the missing words, using the same seven letters in each case.

He ******* to be ******* as a wonderful shot.
He potted a dog and ******* was his lot.

17

LONG WORD

Can you think of an English word of twenty-eight letters ?

18

ALPHABET SENTENCE

2|89   Make up a short sentence containing all the letters of the alphabet.

19

WHAT IS IT ?

What we caught we threw away.
What we could not catch we kept.

20

TRANSLATE THIS

YYURYYUBICURYY4ME

21

SUBTRACTION

Take 9 from 6
   ,, 10 ,, 9
   ,, 50 ,, 40
   and leave 6.

22

CATS

A hexagonal room had a cat in each corner, five cats before each cat and a cat on every cat's tail. How many cats were there in the room ?

23
THE SCAVENGER

A scavenger who made a habit of picking up cigarette ends, found that he could make one cigarette out of seven ends. One night he arrived home with forty-nine ends, and the next day, being Sunday, he made them up into cigarettes and smoked them all himself. How many did he smoke that Sunday?

24
CHAIN WELDING

A man brought five pieces of chain, each of three links, to a shopkeeper and asked him to have them made into one continuous chain. The shopkeeper quoted him one penny per cut and one penny per weld, and said that it would therefore cost eight cents. As the blacksmith charged the shopkeeper one penny per cut and one penny per weld, how did the shopkeeper make a profit on the transaction?

25
THE PORTRAIT

Madam Blawstyer, pointing to a portrait, said :
" I've no sister or brother, you may think me wild ; but that man's mother was my mother's child."
What relation was madam to the man in the picture?

26
WHISKY AND WATER

One tank is half full of water, and another half full of whisky. A spoonful of water is taken from the first tank and mixed with the whisky in the second. A spoonful of the watered whisky is then taken and mixed in the tank of water. Is the amount of water taken from the first tank greater or less than the amount of whisky taken from the second tank?

27

A SURPRISING PERMUTATION

If three married women are seated in fixed positions round a table, there is only one possible way to seat their husbands so that men and women alternate and no husband is next to his wife. With four couples there are two possible arrangements. How many possible arrangements are there with five couples, with six, and with ten couples?

28

ROPE AND PULLEY

A rope passes over a pulley, and a weight of 150 lb. is fixed to one end of it. A man weighing 150 lb. starts to climb steadily up the rope. Will the weight rise or fall?

29

TRAIN PROBLEM

Suppose the journey between New York and Boston takes four and a half hours and *vice versâ*, and that a train starts from each city every hour on the hour. How many trains from Boston will a passenger from New York to Boston meet and pass on the journey?

30

THE LOST SACKS

A dealer buys in the market a number of sacks of chicken food for $2.40. On his way home two of the sacks fall off the cart and are lost. He sells the remainder for $2.52, and makes two cents profit on each sack sold. How many sacks did he buy in the market?

31

CONSTABLE BOSSEYE'S FAMILY

In 1914, the year war broke out, Constable Bosseye's age added to that of his wife was ten times the sum of the ages of all their children. In the year 1916 it was only six times the sum, and in 1922 it had fallen to three times the sum. How many children have they? (They are all alive.)

32

MOTOR HIRE

Michael O'Bleary hired a motor-car at a cost of fifteen dollars to take him to Ballygoogly market and back again in the evening. When he got half-way on his outward journey he met a friend, gave him a lift to the market, and brought him back to the point where he picked him up in the morning. There was a dispute about the payment. How much should Michael charge his passenger for his share of the motor hire?

33

A RING ROUND THE EARTH

Suppose the distance round the equator is 25,000 miles, and that the surface is quite smooth and circular in section. If a steel band is made to fit tightly round it and then cut, and a piece eighteen feet long is welded into it, how loose will the ring then be? In other words, what will be the size of the gap all round between the inside of the ring and the earth's surface?

34

THE EXPLORERS

Four explorers make a journey into the desert. Each man carries enough food to last him five days. After the party has gone some distance, one man starts back, taking with him just enough food to last him until he gets back to his starting point. Then a second man does likewise, and so on. How many days' journey can the last man make into the desert and return safely? It is assumed that food can be transferred from person to person, and that each man travels in units of full days.

35

THE GAMBLERS

When Ginns and Itts started to play roulette, for every five dollars that Ginns had, Itts had eight. At the end of the play each had won nine dollars, and for every eight dollars that Ginns had, Itts had eleven. How many dollars did each start with?

36

RIDDLE BY LEWIS CARROLL

A Russian had three sons. The first named RAB became a lawyer. The second, YMRA, became a soldier. The third became a sailor. What was his name?

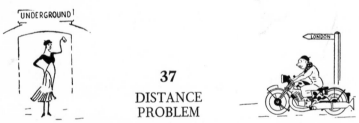

37

DISTANCE PROBLEM

Percy Poppon had an appointment in London at two o'clock in the afternoon. If he left his home and travelled at 15 miles per hour, he would arrive at one o'clock, and if he travelled at 10 miles per hour he would not arrive until three o'clock. What was the distance from his home to London?

38

THE CASE OF ORANGES

Four women bought between them a case containing 233 oranges. They divided them up as follows. Mary had 20 more than Jane, 53 more than Kate and 71 more than Eliza. How many oranges did each woman take?

39

THE BRICK

If a brick weighs 9 lbs. and half a brick, what is the weight of a brick and a half?

40

THE BIRD FANCIER

A man buys 20 birds for 20 cents. Pigeons cost four cents each, larks a half-cent each, and sparrows a fourth-cent each. How many of each kind did he buy?

41

THE FIELD

(1) A farmer had a square field as shown in the illustration, but had to sell the quarter shown shaded. When he died his executors split up the remainder in such a way that each of the farmer's four sons received equal portions, and all exactly the same shape. How was this done?

(2) If the farmer had sold the triangular piece shown by the dotted lines, how would the executor have had to divide up the remainder?

42

THE PENSIONER

When the welfare worker asked the old man what his age was, he replied that "he couldn't rightly remember." He knew, however, that he was sent to school when he was four-and-a-half years of age, and that he stayed at that same school for one-sixth of his life. Then he was in the army for one-fifth of his life, and when he left the army he spent one-quarter of his life as a publican. He had then spent one-third of his life in retirement. What was his age?

43

THE LIBRARY

In a certain library no two books have the same number of words. The number of books in the library is greater than the number of words in the largest book in the library. How many words does one of the books contain, and what is the book about?

44

EVEN NUMBER

We all know that ten is an even number. Prove it ! !

45

WEIGHTS PROBLEM

Find the weights required to weigh any amount from $\frac{1}{2}$ lb. to 60 lb. to the nearest $\frac{1}{2}$ lb. How would you weigh 7 lb. with these weights?

46

THE EIGHT-GALLON CASK

A publican has an eight-gallon cask of beer which he wishes to divide into two four-gallon lots. He has only a five-gallon and a three-gallon measure. How does he do it?

47

MEASURING PROBLEM

A man has two measures, one 7 pint and one 8 pint. How can he use these to measure all quantities from 1 to 8 pints? (to the nearest pint).

48

THE SIX LUMPS OF SUGAR

The illustration shows three coffee cups. You are given six lumps of sugar, and are required to place them in the three cups so that each cup shall contain an uneven number of lumps. All six lumps must be used. How is this possible?

49

CUTTING THE LINOLEUM

The illustration shows a sheet of linoleum. How would you cut it so that it would cover a square floor? The pattern of the squares must match perfectly as in the original piece.

50

ONE HUNDRED

Using the nine digits 1 to 9, and common arithmetical signs, form an expression equal to 100.

51

ONE HUNDRED

Using the ten digits 1, 2, 3, 4, 5, 6, 7, 8, 9, 0, and common arithmetical signs, form an expression equal to 100. There are many easy solutions to this problem.

52
WHICH AND WHY
Which is the heavier, a pound of feathers or a pound of gold?

53
BUYING WHISKY
If whisky were sold by weight, when would you lay in a stock?

54
THE MISSIONARIES AT THE FERRY
Three cannibals and three missionaries have to cross a river. Cannibals, for obvious reasons, must never outnumber missionaries, and only one cannibal can row. Assuming that the boat can hold three passengers, how is the journey made?

55
SHUNTING PROBLEM

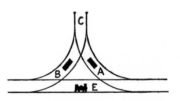

E is an engine on the main line. A and B are waggons on the two sidings. The portion C is only long enough to contain one waggon or the engine. You are required, by means of the engine, to move B to A and A to B and to leave E in its original position. How would you do the shunting if portion C is not long enough for the engine?

56
THE MANX CAT
A passenger on the railway platform said to the stationmaster, "that's a nice Manx cat you've got there." The stationmaster replied, "that's not a Manx cat; that was the nine-twenty that was." What did he mean?

57

THE FISHERMEN

Two fishermen caught a large fish and wished to know its weight. They set a plank up as a see-saw, and one standing on each end, they moved the plank until it was exactly balanced. They then changed places, and the lighter man put the fish on his side of the plank. This just brought the balance exactly right again. The weights of the fishermen were 120 and 150 lb. What was the weight of the fish?

58

THE AGE OF THE JONES'S

Old man Jones's age added to that of his daughter was 100 years. Jones's age multiplied by four and divided by nine gave a figure which was equal to his daughter's age. What were their ages?

59

ANN'S AGE

James is 24 years old. James is twice as old as Ann was, when James was as old as Ann is now. How old is Ann now?

60

MISSING WORDS

In the following rhyme three of the words are missing. These words each contain the same six letters.

Through the ****** trees
Softly coo the doves;
Let a ****** breeze
****** youthful loves.

61

PAWNING THE TEN-DOLLAR POSTAL MONEY ORDER

A traveller returning to New York found that he had only a ten-dollar postal money order, and that his train fare was seven dollars. The ticket clerk refused to accept the money order, so the traveller went across the road to a pawn shop and pawned it for seven dollars. On his way back to the station he met a friend, who, to save the traveller the trouble of returning to redeem the money order, bought the pawn ticket from him for seven dollars. The traveller then bought his ticket and still had seven dollars when he got to New York. Who made the loss?

62

ADDING UP TO 100

Take any integer (1 to 9). Write it down four times, and connect up by arithmetical signs so that the expression will equal 100.

63

ESCAPING PRISONER

A prisoner escapes from Dartmoor Prison, and has half-an-hour's start of two warders and a bloodhound who race after him. The warders' speed is 4 miles per hour; the dog's 12 miles per hour, but the prisoner can only do 3 miles per hour. The dog runs up to the prisoner and then back to the warders, and so on back and forth until the warders catch the prisoner. How far does the dog travel altogether?

64

CLOCK FACE

In a motoring accident the clock on the dashboard was smashed. The owner noticed that the dial was broken into four pieces and that the Roman numerals on each piece added to exactly twenty. Where was the dial broken?

65

THE PATCHWORK QUILT

A number of young ladies, assisted by the curate's elderly sisters, made a patchwork quilt for charity. The work was finished in two months. To celebrate the event, each young girl kissed each other young girl once, and the curate, who was present, kissed each of his sisters once. There were 81 kisses in all. If the curate's sisters had not formed part of the workers, how much longer would the work have taken?

66

SELLING EGGS

This old problem never fails to interest. A market woman sold to Mr. Jones half her stock of eggs and half an egg. She then sold to Smith half of her remaining stock and half an egg. Then Robinson bought half of the eggs which she had left and half an egg. Finally Brown then bought the rest of her stock, namely thirty-three. How many eggs did she have to start with? She did not sell any broken eggs.

SECTION TWO

NOT SO EASY PROBLEMS

"Now unmuzzle your wisdom."

Solutions on p. 116

NOT SO EASY PROBLEMS

67
THE COLUMN OF TROOPS

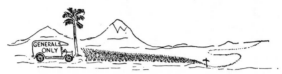

A COLUMN of troops one mile long is moving along a road at a uniform pace. A messenger is sent from the head of the column, delivers a message at the rear of the column and returns. He also moves at a uniform pace and arrives back at the head of the column when it has just covered its own length. How far does the messenger go?

68
RECTANGULAR FIELD
A field is of such proportions that the length is to the breadth as the diagonal is to the length. The breadth is 100 feet. What is its area in square feet?

69
THE CYCLE RACE
A cyclist practising for a road race found that one complete circuit of the course took him exactly two hours and fifteen minutes. The course at one part was very hilly. He knew that his speed on the level was at the rate of 16 miles per hour, uphill it was 12 miles per hour, and downhill 24 miles per hour. What was the distance round the course?

70
THE FOUR FOURS

Make all numbers from 1 to 100 by means of four 4's and common arithmetical signs. Never less and never more than four 4's. For example:

$$1 = \frac{44}{44} \qquad 2 = \frac{4+4}{\sqrt{4}+\sqrt{4}} \qquad 3 = \frac{4+4+4}{4}$$

and so on. Decimals, roots and powers may be used, but no words. (All numbers up to 200 have been determined.)

71
LADDER PROBLEM

A is a box 2 feet each way. B is a ladder 10 feet long. The ladder rests on the ground and touches the wall and the edge of the box, as shown in the illustration. What is the distance D from the bottom of the ladder to the wall? This problem may be solved by a quadratic equation.

72
THE CANNON BALLS (C.E.P.S.)

There are three cannon balls of different sizes and all are hollow. The external and internal diameter of each ball is an exact number of centimetres, and all the balls are the same weight. What are their sizes?

73
CLOCK PROBLEM

At what time between 3 and 4 o'clock will the hands of a clock be in a straight line?

74
MARY AND JANE

The combined ages of Mary and Jane are 44 years. Mary is twice as old as Jane was when Mary was half as old as Jane will be when Jane is three times as old as Mary was when Mary was three times as old as Jane. What are their ages?

75

NINE UNKNOWNS

If the letters A B C D E F G H J represent single and different integers, solve the following :

$$\frac{ABC}{3} = JE \qquad \frac{DEF}{6} = JE \qquad \frac{GHJ}{9} = JE$$

76

LINOLEUM CUTTING

A man had a square of linoleum, the sides of which measured something between 100 and 200 inches. He then bought another square, which was exactly 1 inch longer on each side. He cut the squares up in such a way that when he put all the pieces together they formed a larger square. What was the size of each original square ? What is the smallest number of cuts required to make the two small squares into one larger square ?

77

INSURANCE

Sir Dibley Dilnot took out a policy of insurance for his son's benefit, on the son's first birthday. Under the scheme the first premium was $1 and the premiums increased by $1 each year. At the end of a number of years the son found that the amount already paid in premiums was equal to the amount which would still have to be paid before the sum insured would be due for payment. What was the son's age at this period and at what age would the insurance be due ?

78

A GIDDY REVOLUTION

An athlete runs round a fixed central point in a spiral path at the rate of ten miles per hour, the spiral being of such a form that each turn is only half the length of the preceding one. How many times will he go round the centre point in ten minutes if his first circuit takes him half a minute ?

79

THE DOG FANCIERS

Four dog dealers purchase a barge full of dogs.

The first buys one airedale, three spaniels and seven puppies, and pays for this lot $14.

The Second buys one airedale, four spaniels and ten puppies, for which he pays $17.

The Third buys ten airedales, fifteen spaniels and twenty-five puppies ; and

The Fourth buys one airedale, one spaniel and only one puppy.

How much does the third dealer pay, and how much does the fourth pay ?

80

THE OMNIBUS

A fleet of motor buses running between Euston and Waterloo *via* Southampton Row and Aldwych start and arrive every fifteen minutes. A horse bus starts from Euston at the same moment as one of the motor buses. The horse bus travels for twelve-and-a-half minutes before he meets one of the motor buses coming from Waterloo. How long will it be before one of the motor buses coming from Euston will overtake the horse bus ?

81

THE LADDER AND WALL

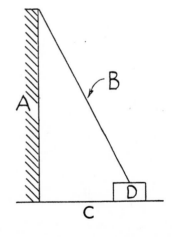

A boy wishing to get to the top of the orchard wall A, brought a ladder B, but he found that the ladder, when placed upright against the wall just reached to the top. So he pulled the foot of the ladder out a distance C, which was exactly 10 feet, and supported it on a box D, which was 2 feet high. The top of the ladder then reached exactly to the top of the wall. What was the height of the wall ?

82

ANOTHER LADDER

Two streets of houses meet at right angles. One is 20 feet wide, and the other 10 feet wide. What is the longest ladder which could be taken round the corner? The ladder must, of course, not be tipped up.

83

PURCHASE OF SHARES

BY C.E.P.S.

Smith, Brown and Robinson, having purchased a penny pencil each, took their wives to a stockbroker's office to buy shares. Mary bought fifty more shares than Brown, and Robinson 120 more than Jane. Each man paid as many shillings per share as he bought shares, and each wife as many pence, and every man, excluding commission and stamps, spent twenty-one shillings more than his wife. What was Eliza's married name?

84

FOUR CANNON BALLS

There are four cannon balls each an exact number of inches in diameter. They are all different in size, and the diameters increase by exactly 1 inch. The weight of the four together is the same as the weight of a cannon ball which is double the diameter of a ball which is 1 inch smaller than the smallest ball. What are the diameters?

85

FIVE CANNON BALLS

There are five cannon balls each being an exact number of inches in diameter. They are all different in size, and the diameters increase by 1 inch. The largest and the smallest ball together have the same weight as the sum of the weights of the three intermediate ones. What are their diameters?

86

TRIANGLE

What is the smallest triangle whose sides are consecutive integers and whose area is exactly divisible by 20 ?

87

A FRACTION

A fraction has a three-figure numerator and a six-figure denominator. All the figures are different. If the fraction is inverted it has the same value as its new denominator. What is the fraction ? Find two solutions.

88

OLD CROCKS MOTOR RACE

In the race to Brighton for motor cars over twenty years old which took place last year, all the competitors had troubles of various sorts on the journey.

If 65 per cent had tire trouble
,, 75 ,, ,, transmission trouble
,, 85 ,, ,, valve trouble
and ,, 95 ,, ,, ignition trouble,

what is the least percentage of the cars which must have had all four troubles ?

89

THE MOTOR BOAT

A motor boat takes five minutes to run from Warsash to the Hamble buoy when going with the tide, and fifteen minutes against the tide. How long would it take at slack water ?

90

MONEY FRACTION

What is the fraction of one pound, of one shilling and of one penny which, when added together, equals one pound ? The fraction is the same in each case.

91

RESTORATION OF DIGITS

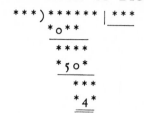

In above division a six-digit number is divided by a three-digit number, which gives a three-digit quotient. Find the numbers.

92

SUBSTITUTION OF DIGITS

In the following division each digit has been used to represent another; this code is consistent throughout. Find the proper digits to satisfy the working.

```
87 ) 65447 | 737
     647
     ―――
     224
     261
     ―――
     647
     647
     ===
```

93

PURCHASE OF AEROPLANES

A certain government has an order to place for a number of aeroplanes, and decides to carry out similar tests on three machines, one from each of three manufacturers which we will call A, B and C. They are to be tested for climbing speed, cost, and bomb-carrying capacity, and the purchaser agrees to buy from the firm whose aeroplane is the best all round in these respects, it being understood that if, for instance, all the machines were alike except that one climbed at double the speed of the others it would be considered twice as good as the others. The tests were as follows:

Test 1.—A's climbs 500 feet while B's climbs 200 feet, but C's climbs 400 feet while A's climbs 300 feet.

Test 2.—One of A's costs as much as 5 of C's, and 3 of C's cost the same as 5 of B's.

Test 3.—One of B's carries the same number of bombs as 4 of C's, and one of A's carries the same number as 3 of B's.

What was the final order of merit of the three machines ?

94
THE FIVE CASKS OF BEER

A bottler had five empty casks and he tried the following experiment :

First he filled up 1 and 2 with beer, and found that together they held 10½ gallons. Then he poured the beer from 1 into 3, and to fill up 3 he had to add another 3½ gallons. He then poured 2 into 4, and had to add another 1½ gallons to completely fill 4. Then he poured 3 into 5, and to fill 5 he was obliged to add another 1½ gallons. Then he filled 3 from 4, but as he had some left over in 4 he put it into 1. He then found that to fill 1 he had to add another 3½ gallons. What was the capacity of each cask ?

95
PARCEL POST

Parcel post rules are that the longest parcel which may be sent is 3 feet 6 inches, and that the maximum combined length and girth is 6 feet. What is the size and shape of the box which will contain the greatest volume ? What is the shape and size of parcel which will contain the greatest volume ?

96
CATCHING A HORSE

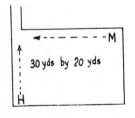

A man and a horse are in a field 30 yards and 20 yards respectively from an opening leading into a lane in the corner. The man and horse start running towards the opening at the same time. The horse travels four yards while the man travels three yards. The horse therefore reaches the opening before the man. What is the shortest lasso which will enable the man to catch the horse ?

97

THE SPIDER ON THE FLOOR

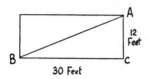

The diagram shows the floor plan of a room 12 feet by 30 feet. A spider at A wishes to crawl over to the opposite corner B. If he walks round by the baseboard *viâ* C, the distance is 42 feet. If, on the other hand, he walks direct from A to B, the distance is shorter, but owing to the difficulty of walking on the thick carpet, he finds that it takes him as long to walk 3 feet in this direction as it does to walk 4 feet round by the bare skirting board. What route should he take so that he may get from A to B in the shortest time?

98

THE FOUR GOATS

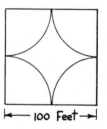

Four goats are tethered one at each corner of a square field 100 feet by 100 feet. The tethers are of such length that each goat can graze over a sector of 50 feet radius. They therefore are compelled to leave uneaten a portion in the centre of the field. Three of the goats are sold, and the farmer lengthens the tether of the remaining goat. He found that he had made it just the length to allow the goat to graze over exactly the same area as all the four goats had previously. What was the length of the tether?

99

FOLDING A SQUARE FROM A RECTANGLE

You are given a rectangle of paper ABCD, the dimensions of which are unknown. You are required to determine the side of a square which has an area equal to the rectangle by merely folding the paper three times. This difficult problem has a very elegant solution.

100

CROSSED LADDERS

In a narrow street a ladder 30 feet long has its foot at one side of the street and rests against the house on the opposite side. A second ladder, 20 feet long, crosses from the opposite side of the street in the same way. The point where the two ladders cross is exactly 6 feet from the ground. What is the width of the street?

MATCH AND COIN GAMES

"Those who are quick in deciding are in danger of being mistaken."

Solutions on p. 118

SECTION THREE

MATCH AND COIN GAMES

101

THE NINE DOTS

· · ·
· · ·
· · ·

MARK on a piece of paper nine dots in three rows of three, as shown :

The problem is to join them all up with four strokes of a pencil without lifting the pencil from the paper.

102

THE SIXTEEN DOTS

· · · ·
· · · ·
· · · ·
· · · ·

Join up 16 dots in 4 rows of 4 dots, with six strokes.

103

THE SIXTY-FOUR DOTS

· · · · · · · ·
· · · · · · · ·
· · · · · · · ·
· · · · · · · ·
· · · · · · · ·
· · · · · · · ·
· · · · · · · ·
· · · · · · · ·

Join up 64 dots in 8 rows of 8 dots, with fourteen strokes.

104

NINE MEN'S-MORRIS

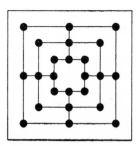

This ancient game is played outdoors with stones, or indoors with coins or counters. Each of the two players has nine counters, and plays a counter in turn on the black dots. Each tries to get three of his counters in a line. The player who succeeds in this removes one of his opponent's men from the board. When all the men are played down on the board each player in turn pushes a man along the lines one space at a time, always trying to get three of his men in line.

ARRANGEMENTS OF COUNTERS
105
Lay down 21 coins in 12 rows of 5 coins.

106
Lay down 11 coins in 16 rows of 3 coins.

107
Lay down 12 coins in 7 rows of 4 coins.

108
Lay down 22 coins in 21 rows of 4 coins.

109
Lay down 21 coins in 11 rows of 5 coins.

110
THE LAST OF FIFTY COUNTERS

Lay fifty counters out in ten heaps of five each. Each of two players playing alternately chooses any heap, and takes all that heap or any number from it as he pleases. The loser is the player who is obliged to take the last counter.

111
SPINNING A COIN

With a sharp knife cut into one side of the edge of a penny, thus leaving a small splinter sticking up. If you spin the penny on its edge on a table, you can tell which side (head or tail) will be uppermost by the difference in the sound made as the coin is settling down. You can turn your back to the table while the coin is spinning and give the answer, head or tail, without any chance of error.

112
SIX COINS IN A RING

Lay six pennies down on the table in two columns, as shown. The game is to change them into a ring in three moves only. One coin only may be moved at a time, and when it is placed in its new position it must be touching two other coins.

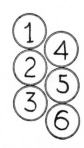

113

TURNING OVER THE DIME

Hold the left hand back upwards and horizontal, and with the fingers half closed. Lay a dime on the last joint of the third finger close to the knuckles. Close the left thumb towards the palm and bring it behind the first joint of the third finger. Press the point of the third finger on to the thumbnail. You are now ready to demonstrate the power of your muscles. To do this press the third finger closer to the palm and allow it to slip over the thumb. This will give a sudden upward jerk to the back of the third finger, and the coin will turn over.

114

THE EIGHT-POINTED STAR

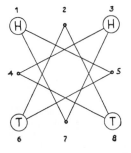

Place coins head upwards on 1 and 3 and tails upwards on 6 and 8. The game is to move the coins along the lines (they must be moved one at a time, but in each move a coin may be moved along more than one line in succession) so as to get heads up on 6 and 8, and tails up on 1 and 3. Seven moves are required.

115

TRAIN OF PENNIES

Lay down about twelve pennies in a perfectly straight line (use a book as a guide) and touching each other. Put your fore-finger down on the 12th penny and slide the coin to the right about 1 inch away from the column. Then bring it up sharply to strike the 11th penny. The column will remain stationary, but the 1st penny will be shot to the left away from number 2. Then place the pennies back again in close column, and with the 1st and 2nd fingers slide the 11th and 12th coins to the right, and bring them smartly up to the column. It will be found that the 1st and 2nd pennies will now move away to the left. Try again with three or four coins.

116
MATCH SQUARES

Lay down sixteen matches to form five squares as shown. The problem is to move three matches to form four squares only. The four squares must be the same size.

117

MATCH TRIANGLES

Lay down sixteen matches to form ten triangles. Remove four matches and leave four triangles only.

118
MATCHES AND CORK

Lay down four matches on a table and place a cork on them in such a position that the heads of the matches do not touch the cork or the table. The cork must not touch the table.

119
SPINNING A HALF DOLLAR

Set a coin on its edge on a table and hold it there by pressing it down with your left 1st finger. Lay your right 1st finger on the top of your left, and with your right thumb as shown in the illustration. Pretend to generate electricity by rubbing up and down

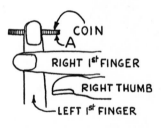

the back of your left finger with your right. Then suddenly push your right finger down your left and past its tip. Your thumb, as it passes, will catch the side of the coin at A, thus setting it spinning on its edge.

120
HEADS TO TAILS

Lay down eight coins in a circle all heads up. Start from any coin which is heads up, count "one," "two," "three," "four," and turn this fourth coin tails up. Do this until all the coins but one are tails up.

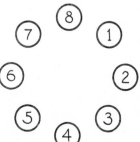

121
ODD OR EVEN

If any number of coins are placed on a table by your audience (the number is unknown to you) you can offer, to add coins to the pile so that if the number is an even one you will make it into an odd number, or if it is an odd number you will make it into an even one. How is this done?

122
SPINNING A COIN

If you pick up any milled-edge coin on the points of two pins you may spin it between the points by blowing against the lower half.

123
THE COIN CROSS

Lay down seven coins to form a cross. This counts five vertically and three horizontally. You are required by lifting two coins only and replacing them to make the horizontal and the vertical arm count up to the same number.

124
EIGHT HEADS AND EIGHT TAILS

Lay down sixteen coins, heads and tails alternately as shown. The problem is to re-arrange the coins so that those in each vertical column are alike. Two coins only, may be touched.

125
THE THIRTY-TWO COINS

The illustration shows thirty-two coins set out in a square with nine coins on each side. The problem is to remove four coins and still count nine coins on each side. Then remove another four coins, which will leave twenty-four, and re-arrange them to still count nine on each side. Remove four more coins, thus leaving twenty coins, and re-arrange these twenty to count nine on each side.

126
THE FIFTEEN MATCH GAME

Fifteen counters or matches are placed on the table. Two persons playing alternately each take one, two, or three, as he chooses. The player who finally holds an uneven number is the winner. For example, if A finally has seven and B has eight, then A is the winner. The first player A can always win if he takes two at the start. Then if at any time he has an even number in his hand he should leave 4, 5 or 12 for B, and if he has an odd number in his hand, he should leave 1, 8 or 9 for B.

127
REVOLUTION OF ONE PENNY ROUND ANOTHER

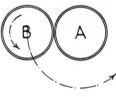

Place two pennies down on the table touching each other. If B revolves once round A by rolling on its edge, how many revolutions does B make around its own centre.

BLACK

128
SIMPLE CHESS PROBLEM

White to play, moves each of his pieces once only and mates.

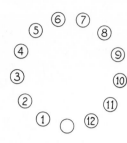

129

REVERSING NUMBERED COUNTERS

Lay down twelve numbered counters in a circle and one vacant space. The game is by moving the counters one at a time as in draughts, *i.e.*, into a vacant space, or by jumping over an adjacent counter into a vacant space, to reverse the numbers to read anti-clockwise. Backward and forward moves are allowed. Forty-four moves are necessary.

A	B	C
D	E	F
G	H	I

130

KNIGHTS' MOVES

Place two black knights in cells A and C, and two white knights in cells G and I. With knights' moves, exchange the positions of the black and white men.

131

REVERSING SIX COUNTERS

The game is to reverse the order of the counters to read backwards and with the blank space at the left as at the start. A counter may be moved into a blank adjacent space or jump over the next counter into a vacant space. Backward and forward moves are allowed. Twenty-one moves are required.

132

COIN COUNTING

Throw nine coins down on the table, remove four of them. Add three coins and leave seven.

133
SIMPLE PAWN GAME

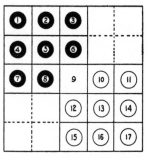

Place two black and two white men at the opposite sides of a chess board. Each player can move over any number of squares backwards or forwards one piece at a time. The object is to drive your opponent back to his original position.

134
CHECKERBOARD PROBLEM

In this problem you are required to inter-change all the white and black men. The black men can only move from left to right or downwards. The white men can only move from right to left or upwards. No diagonal or backward moves are allowed, and all the men must be kept within the squares shown in full lines. Forty-six moves are required.

135

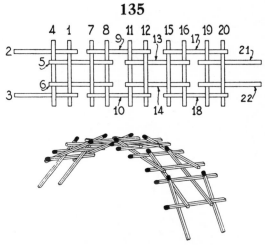

BRIDGE OF MATCHES

Lay large kitchen matches down in the order shown by the numbers 1 to 22.

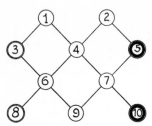

136
FOUR COINS

Place a coin on 3 and on 8, heads up, and a coin on 5 and on 10, tails up. The problem is to interchange the coins by sliding them one at a time along the lines. At no time may a head and a tail coin stand on the same line. Eighteen moves are required.

137

THE FIVE PEAS

In this effective little trick the performer shows five peas in the palm of his right hand. He takes one up in his left finger and thumb and wets it with his tongue. He closes his right hand and rests the pea (to dry) as shown in the illustration. Then he picks it up and places it in his right ear. Then he opens his right hand, shows that there are only four peas left. He takes one up and goes through the same performance, putting this one in his left ear. When he opens his hand finally and shows the last pea, he puts it into his mouth. Then he opens his mouth and shows all five peas on his tongue. This is the rhyme which goes with it :

Five little peas you here do see
These my mother gave to me
First she told me to take one up
Taste it and put it there to dry
Then she told me to take it up
And put it in that ear.

Four little peas you here do see
These my mother gave, etc., etc.

Three little peas you here, etc.

Two little peas, etc.

One little pea you here do see
This my mother gave to me
Then she told me to take it up
and eat it.

138

TWO PENNIES UNDER THE TABLE

Lay two pennies on a table in front of you close and parallel to the edge, and about 9 inches apart. With your right hand lift the right penny, place it in the palm of your left hand, and close your fingers tightly on it. When doing this keep your left hand directly over the point where the right hand coin lies, *i.e.*, in line with your right shoulder. This is important, as it is in the next move that the misdirection necessary to the success of this trick depends. Now take up the left coin in your right hand and close your fingers over it. As your right hand comes forward to lift the left coin, move your left fist towards you and over the edge of the table to make room for your right hand to pick up the left coin, and quietly drop the penny from the left fist into your lap. When you have picked up the left coin in your right hand, bring the left palm smartly down in the middle of the table, saying : " I now place this coin down on the table." Put the right hand under the table saying : " And I put this coin under the table." When you have done this, pick up with your right hand the coin which is lying in your lap. Then explain in appropriate patter that you are going to pass the coin through the table. Lift the left hand and show that the coin has disappeared, and bring the right hand from under the table, open it and show both coins. If this trick is well done it is most effective.

139

THE MATCH MULTIPLYING LEVER

Lay match A down on the table, and on the top of it match B at the angle shown. Then lay C on the top of B, D on C, and so on. Match A should be moved close up to C, so that the head of B is touching the table. The head of C will therefore, if the balance is correct, be lifted away from the table. If you now press down on match F with your fore-finger, the head of the match B will rise up from the table.

140

QUARTER IN THE LAKE

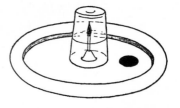

Lay a quarter on a flat plate (to one side) and pour in a little water to barely cover it. You are required to remove the quarter with one finger without wetting it. To do this, set a candle upright in the centre of the plate (stick it in a piece of potato) and light it. Cover the lighted candle with a tumbler. When the edge of the glass is under water the pressure of the atmosphere will force the water up into the glass and leave the quarter high and dry.

141

THE BALANCED HALF DOLLAR

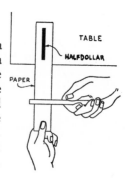

Lay a strip of paper down on the edge of a smooth table and balance a coin on its edge (a half dollar is best) on the paper as shown in the illustration, or at right angles to this. Grip the end of the strip of paper in the left hand, and holding a pencil in the right hand, bring the pencil down on the paper with a smart blow. The paper will be pulled away and the coin will remain securely balanced on its edge on the table.

142

JOSEPHUS PROBLEM

This old story tells that the crew of a ship consisted of 15 of the captain's relatives and 15 of his wife's relatives. Owing to a leak in the ship it was necessary to lighten her, so the captain placed the 30 men in a circle. He counted round and round and threw every tenth man overboard. In what order did he place the crew so that all of his wife's relatives went overboard first?

143

COINS ON ELBOW

Place a pile of coins on your elbow in the position shown in the illustration. Bring your hand down sharply and catch the pile of coins before they reach the ground.

144

HOW MANY ARE LEFT?

To tell how many coins or cards are left in a row. Ask someone to lay down two rows of coins, the lower row to contain fewer coins than the upper one, and to let you know the difference. Then ask him to take away (say) four coins from the lower row, to take as many from the upper row as there are left in the lower row, and then to take away all the coins in the lower row. You can then tell him how many coins are left in the upper row. Can you find out how this is done?

145

ELECTRIC SHOCK

Push two matches into one end of a match box, and one into the other end, as shown in the illustration. Explain to the most credulous person in the room that you are going to give him an electric shock with the match box. Ask him to hold the two matches, one between the finger and thumb of each hand, and to hold them very tightly. He is also to see that both his feet are on the ground. You then push the single match out and in to generate the electricity. Ask him if he feels anything. He will say "no." Then ask him to lift one foot off the ground while you try again. Pump vigorously and ask him if he now feels anything. He will again say "no." You then ask him if he does not even feel his leg being pulled!

146

THE KISSING MATCH

Take the bottom out of a wooden match box and split it down the centre with the grain. Then bend each piece back about one-quarter of its length from the end. Set the two pieces on a table on the short ends as shown in the illustration. If you put a drop of water between the two bends the long pieces will gradually come together.

147

REVERSING THE MATCH BOX

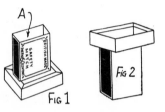

Place the empty tray of a match box open side downwards on the table, and lay the case on the top of it as shown in Fig. 1. The problem is to get the two parts into the position shown in Fig. 2. You may touch the case with your finger and thumb, but you must not touch the tray.

148

COINS IN WINE GLASS

Place a dime and a half dollar in a *conical* wine glass as shown. If you blow strongly down on the half dollar, it will turn over and the dime will be blown out on to the table. With a little less strength the dime will rest on the top of the half dollar.

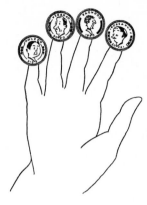

149
HALF DOLLARS AND FINGERS

Place a half dollar on the tip of each finger. Try to work them all in a pile on the tip of your first finger. You must not use your thumb, nor, of course, your left hand.

150
LIGHTING A CIGARETTE

A cigarette may be lit quite easily by holding it 4 or 5 inches above the flame of the match.

151
NOT LIGHTING A CIGARETTE

Strike a match and secretly break it in two between your finger and thumb. If you roll it round between your finger and thumb it will easily separate into two parts. Then hand the match to your friend, the unlighted end towards him. He will take it to light his cigarette while you light your own with the other end.

152
HALF DOLLAR IN TUMBLER OF WATER

Borrow a half dollar, place it in the centre of a handkerchief, grip it by its edge, and let the handkerchief fall down over it. Give the coin to someone to hold over a glass three-quarters full of water, the handkerchief, of course, covering the tumbler. At the word "go" ask him to drop the coin into the tumbler. The noise which it makes in falling will be distinctly heard. When the handkerchief is removed the coin has disappeared from the tumbler.

The secret of this trick is to have a disc of glass the size of a half dollar which you substitute for the real coin as you turn the handkerchief over it. The glass coin will not be seen in the water. This very old trick never fails to mystify those who are not in on the secret.

153

BLOWING A COIN OUT OF A WINE GLASS

Set two conical wine glasses side by side and drop a dime into one of them. Blow down strongly on the dime, and it will hop out of one glass and into the other.

154

PENNIES IN TUMBLER OF WATER

Fill a tumbler with water. With care you may drop a large number of pennies into the tumbler before the water overflows.

STRONG MAN TRICKS

"Let there be jesting without bitterness."

STRONG MAN TRICKS

155

SCISSORS CUT PAPER

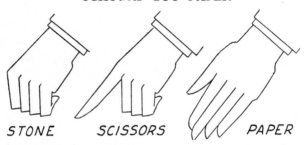

STONE   SCISSORS   PAPER

THIS old game is a form of drawing lots. Two players first of all hold their right fists up to their shoulders. They bring them down sharply at the word " go " until their forearms are horizontal, and can do one of three things.

(1) Keep the fist closed. This represents a *stone.*
(2) Open out the forefinger. This represents *scissors.*
(3) Open out all fingers and thumb. This represents *paper.*

The players have six shots. If each has three wins it is a tie, and the next turn decides the winner. The points are counted as follows : " Stone " blunts " scissors," but can be covered by " paper." " Scissors " cut " paper," but are blunted by " stone."

156

TURNING OVER THE SAUCER

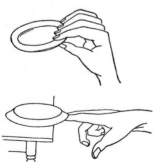

Lay a saucer upside down, letting one edge project over the edge of the table. Place the back of the fingers under the overhanging edge of the saucer, and, with an upward jerk turn it over in the air and catch it with the same hand before it touches the table. This trick is really easier than it looks, as the thumb is kept open ready to grip the saucer as it revolves. In fact, if the operation is smartly performed, the fingers never lose contact with the inside of the saucer. Try it on an upholstered chair before attempting it on a marble-topped table.

157

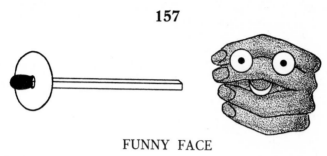

FUNNY FACE

Cut two discs of white card about the size of a dime, and push a match through the centre of each one, bringing the heads close up to the discs. Close the left fist with your thumb or a penny protruding between the second and third fingers. Push one match between the first and second fingers at the third joint until the paper disc rests against the back of the fingers. Push the other match between the same fingers, but at the second joint of these fingers. Drape a handkerchief over your hand, and you will produce a face much more realistic than I have been able to show in the drawing.

158

CATCHING A SHEET OF PAPER

Stand on a chair or ladder. Drop a sheet of paper, and ask someone to catch it fairly between his finger and thumb before it reaches the ground. Not so easy !

159

MATCH-BOX FIGHT

Two opponents stand facing each other, right arms outstretched, left hands behind their backs. A match box is laid on the back of each right hand. The game is to knock your opponent's match box off with your right hand or arm without letting your own fall to the ground.

160

PICKING UP A MATCH BOX

Put a broomstick behind your knees, bring your arms behind it, and place your hands on the ground in front of you. Pick up a match box in your teeth from this position.

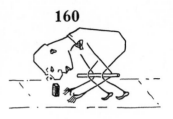

161

LIGHTING A CIGARETTE

Two persons kneel on the ground on one knee and grip the ankle of the other leg. One person has to lift a match box, open it, strike a match and light the other person's cigarette.

162

PICKING UP A CORK

Lay a light chair down on its front legs with its back horizontal. Place a cork on the top rail as shown at A. Kneel on the lower rail and pick up the cork in your teeth.

163

ROUND THE BROOMSTICK

Place a broomstick in the corner of the baseboard as shown in the illustration. Lower your head and get up on the other side of the stick.

164
SUN AND EARTH

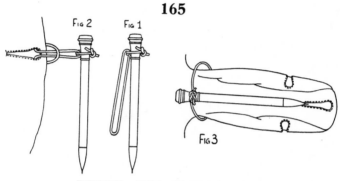

Moisten a plate with water and place the top of an eggshell on the edge as shown. Incline the plate slightly. The shell will slide down the incline and at the same time rotate at a surprising rate. This is a most effective trick, and the shell may be spun round and round by suitably inclining the plate as it revolves.

165

Fɪɢ 2   Fɪɢ 1

Fɪɢ 3

PENCIL AND BUTTONHOLE

Tie a loop of string on to a pencil, making the loop slightly shorter than the length of the pencil, as shown in Fig. 1. The problem is to get it on to your buttonhole as shown in Fig. 2. To do this, bunch up the cloth as shown in Fig. 3, and pass the loop over this lump of cloth. The point of the pencil may then be passed down through the buttonhole, which will bring the string as in Fig. 2. To undo the string reverse the above process.

166
GLASS OF WATER ON THE CEILING

Stand on a high chair which will allow you to touch the ceiling. Place a glass of water up against the ceiling and hold it there by the point of a walking stick. While still on the chair ask someone to hold the stick and to press the glass on to the ceiling. Get down from the chair and move it away out of reach of the person holding the stick. Time the victim's temper with a stop watch.

167

BURNING A LUMP OF SUGAR

If you try to burn a lump of sugar with a match you will find it impossible, as the sugar simply melts away. If, however, you first dip the sugar into cigarette ash it will catch alight quite easily.

168

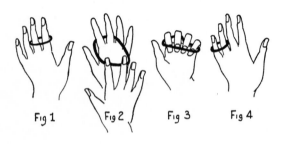

Fig 1   Fig 2   Fig 3   Fig 4

RUBBER BAND TRICK

The effect of this trick is as follows. You place a rubber band round your first and second fingers as in Fig. 1. By closing and opening your hand you instantaneously change the band on to your third and fourth fingers as shown in Fig. 4. To do this pull the band down the palm of your left hand by the first and second fingers of your right hand as shown in Fig. 2. Then close all the fingers of the left hand into this loop as in Fig. 3. You can still show the back of your hand, which of course, will be towards your audience, and they will see that the band is round the first and second fingers only. If you now open your left hand, the band will at once spring on to the third and fourth fingers as in Fig. 4. A little showmanship is of course necessary to bring this trick off successfully.

169

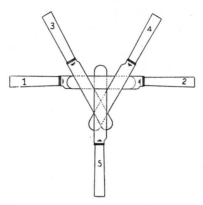

THE FIVE KNIFE BRIDGE

The problem is to lay four knives down on the table and to lift them all together by means of a fifth knife. Lay the four knives down in the order shown and pass the fifth knife over 3 and 4 and under 1 and 2.

170

LIFTING A SPOON

Lift a spoon by the bowl, as shown in the illustration. It is easier to do this with the second finger and thumb.

171

REVOLVING A GLASS OF WATER

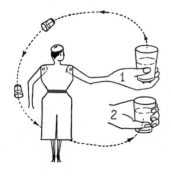

Start by holding the glass of water in your right hand, elbow pointing downwards, as shown in Fig. 1. Revolve it smartly anti-clockwise, as shown by the dotted line and arrows, and finish up gently, as in Fig. 2, with your elbow pointing upwards. Practise this trick out of doors!

172
CENTRIFUGAL FORCE

Tie a jam jar in the middle of a piece of string about 8 feet long. Put some water into the jar and revolve it, on the end of the strings, in a vertical circle in front of you.

173
LIFTING A STOOL

Place a heavy stool or chair on the floor against the wall. Stand 3 feet from the wall. Stoop down and rest your head against the wall. Lift the stool and try to regain an upright position without putting the stool down. The stool must not touch the wall.

174
BLOWING OVER A BIG DICTIONARY

This may be done quite easily by placing the book down on a long thin paper bag. Squeeze up the mouth of the bag round your finger, or tie it round a tube, so as to make an air-tight joint, and blow into it. The bag will expand and overturn the book.

175
BALL UP AN INCLINE

Lay two billiard cues down on the table side by side with the points touching and the butts at such distance apart that a billiard ball will just rest on the table between them. Hold the cues in this position and place a billiard ball down on them near their points. The ball will roll towards the butts, thus apparently travelling up hill by gravity.

176

LIFTING A PAIR OF TONGS

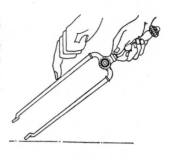

Hold a pair of tongs by the handle in your right hand, noting that the leg which is attached to the handle is uppermost, and rest the points on the ground. To demonstrate the magnetic power in your body you wet the forefinger of your left hand and press it down on the upper leg of the tongs. You then raise your left hand slowly, when the top leg will follow it. Let it fall away from the finger once or twice before you finally succeed in holding it well away from the ground. It is the right hand, of course, which does all the work.

177

REVERSED DRAWING

Lay a piece of paper down in front of a mirror and draw on it a pig, or a square and its diagonals, without looking directly at your hand. You must only look at the image reflected in the mirror.

178

SEVEN MORNING EXERCISES

Toe a line. Kneel down and get up again without using your hands or leaving the line.

179

Clasp your hands together in front of your body and jump through them with both feet.

180

Lie down flat on your back. Fold your arms across your chest and get up on your feet again.

181

Stand facing a wall and put your left toe against it about 2 **feet** from the ground. Hop over your left leg with your right without taking your toe from the wall.

182

Stand close up with your back to a wall and with your heels touching the baseboard. Bend forward and try the impossible task of touching your toes with your fingers.

183

Stand facing a wall and about 3 feet away from it. Lean forward and place the palm of your left hand flat against the wall. Then push with your left hand and so regain your upright position. Increase your distance from the wall and try again.

184

Place three chairs in a row. Lie down, with your back on the middle chair, your feet on the right chair and your head on the left chair. Raise and stiffen up your body, slide the middle chair out, lift it over your body and slide it under your back from the other side.

185

THE WALKING STICK

Hold a walking stick by the ends horizontally in front of you and level with your chest. Ask someone to grasp the stick in the middle with both his hands and to try to shove you backwards. You can easily beat even a very strong man at this game, as, by bending one of your arms slightly you break the force of his pressure.

186
PAPER AND BOTTLE

Stand a bottle on a sheet of paper as shown. The problem is to get the paper away without touching the bottle. To do this pull gently on the paper and hammer on the table with your fist. Each blow causes the bottle to lift slightly, thus allowing the paper to be gradually withdrawn.

187
THE CAPTIVE LOOP

Now sir your coat is off
Your right hand pocketed
While o'er your arm
An endless string
Some three yards round
Hangs like a sling.
Take the string off
But just for fun,
It must be done
Keeping your right hand in its place
And not a smile must stir your face.
Until you find this puzzle out,
No coat shall wrap your back about.

The method of performing this seeming impossibility is to pass the string through the arm hole of the waistcoat over the head down through the other arm hole and over the left hand. It may then be drawn down over the body. It is not possible to do this trick if the person is dressed as in the illustration.

188
ONE BALL OR TWO?

Place a marble on a table. Cross your first and second fingers and roll the marble backwards and forwards between them. You will imagine that there are two balls. If you push your second finger forward until it touches the table you will think that you have pushed your finger down between the two balls.

189
ONE NOSE OR TWO?

Try the last trick by rubbing your crossed
fingers gently up and down the bridge of your
nose. The effect is very marked, especially
when your fingers reach the tip of your nose.

190
HEELS OVER HEAD

Stand behind an armchair and grasp the sides of its back. Put your
head down on to the seat, throw up your heels, turn heels over head
and bring yourself into a sitting position in the chair. Use a strong
chair.

191
KISSING YOUR THUMB

Toe a line. Bend down and place the palm of your hand on the
ground in front of you. Stretch your legs out behind the line and by
bending your arm lower your body parallel to the ground. Kiss the
thumb of the hand which is on the ground. Straighten up your arm,
thus raising your body. Bring your toes up to the line, and get up
again.

192
BREAKING YOUR FOREARM

Pull your right sleeve well down and hold it there with your fingers.
Give your right forearm a smart blow with your left fist and press
this arm against your chest. Let go the fingers of your right hand.
Grip your right hand with your left and pull it gradually towards the

left. Your sleeve will be prevented from moving, and as you pull your right hand to the left, it will look as if your arm has been broken at the elbow.

193
BREAKING YOUR NOSE

Place the palms of your hands together, fingers pointing upwards, and grip your nose between your two forefingers. Put the thumbnail of your right hand behind your upper front teeth. Twist your nose to one side with your forefingers, and click your thumbnail on your teeth by pressing your thumb forward.

194
BREAKING YOUR THUMB

Place your left thumb between the first and second fingers of your left hand, getting it as far through as possible so that the first joint of your thumb lies across your second finger. Then bend the first joint of your right thumb as nearly as possible at right angles and bring this joint up, touching and parallel with the second joint of your left thumb. Separate the hands a little and it will appear as if you had pulled off the first joint of your right thumb. The above three tricks, if well done, are a little too realistic for many people. The illustration shows your hands as you see them. Your audience will, of course, be looking from the other side and slightly downwards from your left.

KNOTS AND STRING GAMES

"Rust of the mind is the blight of the abilities."

195 SAILOR'S KNOTS

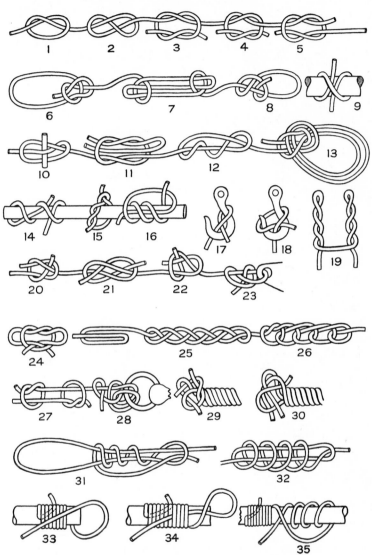

Numbers 1 to 35 show all the Knots in General Use.

1. Overhand knot.
2. Figure of 8 knot.
3. Reef knot.
4. Grannie knot.
5. Tom Fool knot.
6. Bowline.

7. Sheep shank.
8. Running buntline.
9. Clove hitch.
10. Marlin Spike hitch.
11. Bow reef knot.
12. Stevedore's knot.
13. Bowline on a bight.
14. Rolling hitch.
15. Timber hitch.
16. Topsail spar bend.
17. Blackwall hitch.
18. Midshipman's hitch.
19. Catspaw.
20. Sheet bend.

21. Carrick bend.
22. Weaver's knot.
23. Topsail sheet bend.
24. True lovers' knot.
25. Plait knot.
26. Chain knot.
27. Shroud knot.
28. Anchor bend.
29. Wall knot.
30. Crown knot.
31. Hangman's knot.
32. Vanman's knot.
33 and 34. Whipping a rope's
        end.

35. Whipping a rod.

196
FLEMISH LOOP

Cross the cords as shown in Fig. 1 and then pass part A under crossing B and up through the centre space. Pull on A, and the loop will be formed as in Fig. 2. Then slide the two knots together.

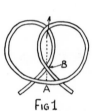

Fig 1

Fig 2

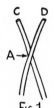

Fig 1

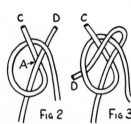

Fig 2   Fig 3

197
SHEET BEND OR WEAVER'S KNOT

The method of making this bend is to cross the ropes as in Fig. 1. Hold the crossing A between the finger and thumb of the left hand and throw the right hand fall of the rope over the thumb, under C and over D, thus making Fig. 2. Pass the end D over two parts, and down under the rope which lies over the thumb of the left hand, thus making Fig. 3.

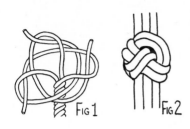

Fig 1   Fig 2

198

THREE-STRAND DIAMOND KNOT

Interlace the three cords as shown in Fig. 1. If the lay is followed round with each cord once more, the double diamond shown in Fig. 2 will be formed.

199

FOUR-STRAND DIAMOND KNOT

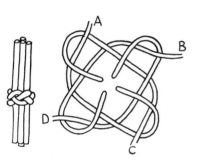

A
B
D
C

The four cords A B C and D should be interlaced as shown, and then rendered up to form the diamond knot shown on the left. If the lay of each cord is followed round, a double or treble diamond can be made.

200

TIMBER RUSTLER'S KNOT

This knot is generally made in a neckerchief. The two ends are interlaced as shown on

the left. The two illustrations on the right show the front and the back of the completed knot.

201

DOUBLE CROWN KNOT

This knot is generally made by unstranding a rope and working the three parts round as shown. See No. 195 (No. 30) for the single form of this knot.

202

DOUBLE CARRICK BEND

203
MAGNUS HITCH

204
MULTIPLE OVERHAND KNOT

205
WHIPPING THE END OF A ROPE

In this modified form, the end B is laid along the rope in a loop which is whipped over by the end A. A is finally passed through the loop made in B. B is then pulled taut.

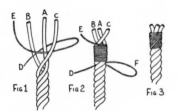

206
WHIPPING THE END OF A ROPE

In this method the rope is un-stranded and a loop of the whip-ping cord, D E, is passed over one strand, A, Fig. 1. The whipping is done by end E, Fig. 2. Loop F is then brought up over A, and tightened down by pulling on D. The ends D and E are then tied with a reef knot on the crown of the rope, thus making Fig. 3.

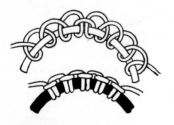

207
ORNAMENTING A RING BY LARK'S HEAD KNOTS

Make right and left half-hitches on a ring, pulling them tight as you pro-ceed. This makes a most effective covering for a ring or eyelet.

208

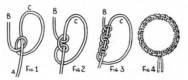

LARK'S HEAD EYELET

This is similar to the preceding, but is made on its own rope. To make it, throw a knot (not shown) on A, and hold this knot in your left hand. Then make a half-hitch on A with the long end B, Fig. 1, and another in the reverse direction, as shown in Fig. 2. Continue making right and left hitches as in Fig. 3. When you have made enough hitches, pull on the end A. This will draw the hitches into a ring as shown in Fig. 4.

209

SHEER LEGS KNOT

Throw down three hitches as shown in Fig. 1. Pass the loops through each other as shown by the dotted lines and arrows, thus making Fig. 2.

210

JAPANESE FANCY KNOT

Interlace the rope as in Fig. 1. Then pull on the loops C and D, thus making Fig. 2.

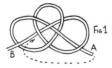

211

BUTTON KNOT

Lay the cord down as in Fig. 1. Follow the first lead round with end A, which will make Fig. 2. Pull on A and B, and render up the cords, making the finished knot, as shown.

212

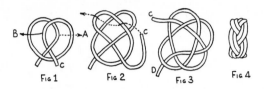

Fig 1   Fig 2   Fig 3   Fig 4

THREE-PART TURK'S HEAD

Lay the cord down as in Fig. 1 and draw loops A and B out on each side as shown, *i.e.*, B over its left loop, and A under its right loop. Pass end C under and over, and under and over, as indicated in Fig. 2, thus making Fig. 3. Follow the lead round with C and D as many times as you like. Fig. 4 shows the finished turk's head.

213

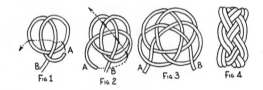

Fig 1   Fig 2   Fig 3   Fig 4

FOUR-PART TURK'S HEAD

This is similar to the above, but it has one more turn. When the turns in Fig. 3 are pushed out into a ring, making Fig. 4, it is quite simple to follow the lead round with the ends A and B as often as you like.

214

JAPANESE FANCY KNOT

This knot which is made by four cords, is formed as shown in Fig. 1. All the parts are drawn up tight to make Fig. 2. This knot is used in combination with others of the same sort to make girdles and sword ornamentations.

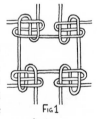

Fig 1

Fig 2

215
CHINESE FLOWER KNOT

Interlace two thumb knots as shown in Fig. 1. Pull the parts A and B out sideways to make Fig. 2. Then pass the loop E down through the centre of the knot, as shown by the dotted line and arrow, which will give you Fig. 3. Tighten up loops A, B, E, F, G to make the finished knot, Fig. 4.

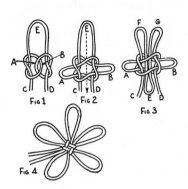

216
MAKING A TWISTED CORD

Take a long piece of worsted and double it in the middle a number of times depending on the thickness you wish to make the finished cord. Get someone to hold one end of the strands while you twist on the other end. Twist the bunch up as tightly as you can. Then double it in the centre, holding the centre with your left hand, and, bringing the two ends together, hold them tightly in your right hand. Let go the centre and shake the bunch smartly. The strands will then twist themselves up into a tight cord.

217
MAN ROPE KNOT

This knot is made by first forming a wall knot on the end of the rope, and then a crown knot, the lay of which is followed round three times. See No. 201.

218
GRUMMET STROP OR QUOIT RING

A piece of four-strand rope is cut four times the length of the circumference of the required ring. This will make four rings. The rope is unstranded very carefully, taking care not to spoil the natural twist of the strands. The single strand is then coiled and twisted round itself as shown in Fig. 1, taking care that the twists lie as they did in the original rope. The two ends where they meet are tucked into the centre of the rope and held in place by a few stitches. Fig. 2 shows the completed ring.

219
ORNAMENTAL KNOT

This knot is sometimes carried out in braid sewn on to a cloth backing.

220
CHINESE FANCY KNOTS

The easiest method of making knots of this kind is to pin the cords down on a cushion or pillow filled with sand. A little practice is required to get the knots symmetrical. Braided blind cord is suitable for making up these knots.

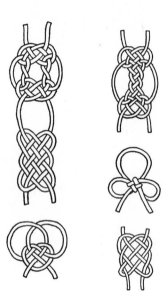

221

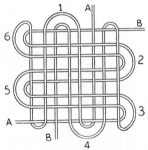

CHINESE BASKET KNOT

This knot is rather complicated to make, and can only be done by pinning the cords down to a cushion or by winding them round a number of nails hammered into a board. It is made from two cords A and B, or from one cord doubled in the centre. When all the interlacing has been done, the loops 1 to 6 are pulled out, thus forming the finished knot shown. In No. 222 this knot is shown in the centre in combination with other fancy knots. It is to be noted that in knot 222 the strings A and B, where they lead in and out of the knot proper, have additional knots formed on them and that the loops are knotted together.

222

CHINESE COMBINATION KNOT

This knot was drawn from the ornamental string on a Chinese smoking pipe. It is a most effective knot, and not so difficult to make as it looks.

223

POINTING A ROPE

This ornamental finish for the end of a rope is made by first putting a seizing round the rope at the part where the pointing is to start from. All the strands are then unlaid, and each strand is further teased out into its yarns. The outside yarns are then temporarily stopped back against the length of the rope, and the inside yarns shaved down to the required taper. The outside yarns are then unstopped, and each one twisted up into a cord. Every other cord is now stopped back and the remainder laid down regularly along the tapered portion. These are bound tightly by three or four turns of twine, the last turn being secured by means of a half-hitch. These cords are now stopped back and the other set is brought down, laid regularly along the tapered portion, and bound with twine.

This is continued, bringing the cords down alternately and gradually reducing the number of cords as the point is reached. When the point is reached, a whipping of twine is passed over all the cords to hold them in place. A coat of varnish or paint is given when all the cords have been hardened down and trimmed up.

224

THREE-STRAND FLAT PLAIT

Pass the right strand over the middle strand and under the left strand, and continue doing this.

225

FIVE-STRAND FLAT PLAIT

Pass the right strand to the left over the next two strands and still to the left under the next two. Then pass the left strand to the right over the next two and still to the right under the next two and so on.

226

SEVEN-STRAND FLAT PLAIT

Pass the outside strands over three and under three, and so on.

227

FOUR-STRAND LARIAT OR SQUARE PLAIT

Take the right outside strand and pass it to the left under the next two strands, and then back towards the right over one strand, thus making it the second strand from the right. Then pass the left outside strand to the right under the next two strands and back towards the left over one strand, thus making it the second strand from the left. Continue with the right outside strand passing it under the next two and back over one. Then do the same with the left outside strand, and so on. The appearance of this plait is as shown at the beginning and end of No. 234, Fig. 2.

228

SIX-STRAND HALF-ROUND PLAIT

Pass the right strand under three and back over one. Then the left strand under three and back over one, and so on. This plait is not much used, as it is not symmetrical.

229

EIGHT-STRAND LARIAT PLAIT

Pass the right strand to the left under the next five strands and then back towards the right over two strands. Do the same with the left strand, and so on. The finished plait is square with a three-part plait on each face.

230

CROWN BRAID

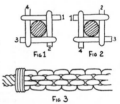

This braid may be made round a rope or stanchion with three, four, or more cords. The illustration shows a four-cord braid. The four cords are seized to the central rope. 1 is laid to the right ; 2 is brought over 1 and to the front ; 3 is brought over 2 and to the left ; 4 is turned back over 3 and passed into the loop made by 1. Fig. 1 shows this first stage, and is a view looking at the end of the central rope. In Fig. 2 1 has been laid over to the left, 4 turned over 1 and brought to the front ; 3 turned over 4 and brought to the right ; 2 turned over 3 and passed through the loop made by 1 when it was turned to the left. This is continued *ad lib.*, and the finished 4-cord braid is as shown in Fig. 3.

231

BRAID WATCH CHAIN

A crown braid made with four flat woven bootlaces and without a central core, is often made up as a watch chain. Square or flat strips of leather may be braided in this way, either with or without a central core.

232

WALL KNOT

To make a wall knot, the rope is unstranded. Each strand is brought under the next strand and then up through the bight made by that strand. The simplest method to make the wall is to hold the rope between the second and third fingers and to lay the strands out on the palm of the hand while holding them down with the thumb.

233

WALL AND CROWN KNOT

The wall and crown is made by first forming a wall and pulling the strands up tight. Each strand is then brought over the next strand and down its bight. By following the lead round with each strand of the crown knot a double or treble crown may be made thus forming the man rope knot, No. 217.

234

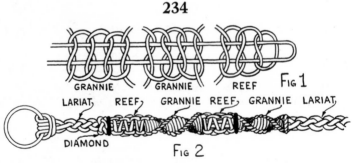

GRANNIE   GRANNIE   REEF   Fig 1

LARIAT,   REEF,   GRANNIE REEF,   GRANNIE LARIAT,

DIAMOND   Fig 2

MAKING A FANCY CORD

Take two pieces of cord twice the length which the finished cord is to be, and double them in the centre. Pass them through a ring or spring hook, as shown on the left of Fig. 2. Fix the ring to a hook in the wall and arrange to fasten the four ends of the cord to a chair so as to hold them taut and horizontal. Start with a four-part lariat plait, No. 227, then a diamond knot, and then another short length of lariat plait if desired. The next part is made by knotting another cord round the four cords, which will then form a core. Fig. 1 shows how this is done. For clearness, only two cords are shown in the core. Start at the middle of the cord with which you are to make the knots, and make about ten reef knots with this cord round the core. These reef knots are shown on the right of Fig. 1. They should be pulled up tight as the work proceeds. Then make about ten left-hand grannie knots, as shown in the middle section of knots in Fig. 1. This will give the left-hand spiral appearance shown in Fig. 2. For the next section another ten reef knots like the first lot should be tied. Then make ten right-hand grannie knots, which will give the right-hand spiral shown in Fig. 2. These grannie knots are shown on the left of Fig. 1. Another diamond knot may now be added and another section of lariat plait. The end may be finished by a man rope knot, or in any other suitable way. The finished cord has a most attractive appearance, and well repays the trouble taken to make it.

235

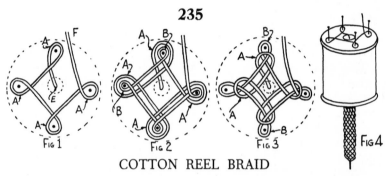

Fig 1   Fig 2   Fig 3   Fig 4

COTTON REEL BRAID

Drive four small nails or pins into the end of a cotton reel, as shown in Fig. 4. Figs. 1, 2 and 3 are enlarged views looking down on the top of the reel, E being the hole in its centre. Pass the end of the string down through the hole E, and wind the end F (which comes from the ball of string) anti-clockwise round the four pins, as shown in Fig. 1. Do not pull the string up tightly, as otherwise you will have some difficulty later on. Then wind the string F round the four pins a second time, making these turns nearer the heads of the pins and slightly tighter than the first turn. This will give you Fig. 2, where A is the first turn, and B the second turn. Then the first four loops A, *i.e.*, the lower turns, should be lifted up with a crochet hook over the heads of the pins, and dropped on the inside. This will give you Fig. 3. The central string, E, should now be pulled down further through the hole in the cotton reel. Then make another turn with F exactly as before, and lift the previous loops over the pins to the centre. Pull on centre string E, and the braid will gradually emerge as shown in Fig. 4. Five or more pins may be used, in which case the braid will be more truly circular. With a larger hole in the centre of a square piece of wood, and about a dozen nails, a string bag may be made. It is perhaps easier at first to wind the string and lift the loops over the pins one at a time. To stop off the braid, pass the end F up through the four loops after they have been removed one at a time from the pegs.

236

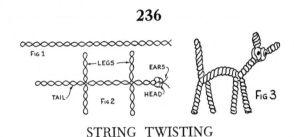

STRING TWISTING

Take a piece of soft string about 15 inches long and get someone to hold one end while you twist up the other end, with the lay, as tightly as you can. Grip the centre of the string, bring the two ends together and hold them with the other hand. Let the centre of the string go, and it will twist up on itself to form a double cord. Fig. 1. Put a knot on the two ends to form the head of the dog as shown in Fig. 2. Then pull the two strings apart at a point about 2 inches from the head. Each side will twist up on itself, thus forming the front legs of the dog. Do the same further down to make the back legs. Bend the head and tail up and the legs down, and you will have Fig. 3. If the completed figure is dipped in size or cellulose varnish, it will keep its shape. Many amusing figures can easily be made by this method. Other figures may be constructed from the kind of pipe cleaners which are made from twisted wire and wool.

237

MULTIPLE THREADING A NEEDLE

Thread the needle and with its point prick a hole in the thread. Then pass the end A through B. Pull on the end A and rotate as shown by the arrow. Each circuit adds another thread through the eye of the needle. When you can get no more through the eye, cut the loop.

238
RINGS OFF A STRING

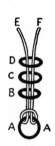

Loop a ring A on to the middle of a string, and run three rings B C and D down the doubled string. Ask someone to hold the two ends, E and F. Explain that the easiest way to remove the four rings is to cut the string where it passes through A. Hold and cover all the rings in your left hand, and with a knife pretend to cut through the string at A. At the same time turn the bottom of the ring towards you and to the top, about the axis A A. This will allow you to remove ring A. Slide the left hand down to A and allow the three rings B C and D to drop into your right hand. Twist the loop at A between your fingers, and ask the person holding the ends E and F to pull these ends apart. He will be surprised to find that the string has been joined up again. You can, if you wish, make a thumb knot with F round E above or below the three rings.

239
FINGER AND THUMB STRING RELEASE

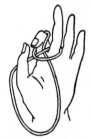

Hang a loop of string over the back of the first and second fingers of the left hand, letting the long loop hang down the palm. Pass the right first finger up through the long loop from below and between the first and second fingers of the left hand. Draw the string on the back of the fingers downwards through the long loop until it is taut. Pass the left thumb over the near string and under the far string, and bring the tip of the left thumb and forefinger together as shown in the illustration. Lift the loop off the second finger, and the string will be released.

240

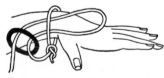

RING AND HANDCUFFS

After the two wrists are tied together with a long string, as in the old manacle trick, draw the centre of the string up into a loop and thread a ring over it. Pass the loop up through the string which encircles the wrist, as shown in the illustration. Lift the loop, giving it an anti-clockwise turn through 180 degrees, over the fingers and thumb, draw it down the palm of the left hand, and under the wrist string. Then lift it back over the

fingers and thumb and pull it down the back of the hand. The ring
will now be firmly knotted on to the string where it passes from one
wrist to the other.

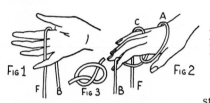

241

KNOTTING A HAND-KERCHIEF WITH ONE HAND

The illustration shows a
string, for the sake of clearness.
Hold your right hand, palm downwards, and lay the string over its
back. Turn your hand, thumb upwards, and bring your little finger
to the near-side of the near string, F, Fig. 1. Then turn your hand
palm downwards, and with a slight swing, grip the back string B
between your first and second fingers, as shown in Fig. 2. Shake the
loops A and C off the back of your hand, and the string will be knotted
as in Fig. 3. With a little practice all these operations can be done
instantaneously and with very good effect.

242

MANY KNOTS

Grip the end of the rope between
the thumb and finger of the left hand,
lead it across the palm and also across
the palm of the right hand. Twist the
fingers of the right hand inwards and
pointing towards you, thus putting a
twist in the rope. Hang the loop thus
made over the fingers of the left hand,
as in Fig. 1. Pass the palm of the
right hand under the fall of the rope,

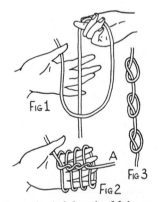

give it a twist as before, and hang the loop on the left hand. Make as
many hitches as you like in this way. The rope on the left hand will
now be as in Fig. 2, except that the hitches need not be drawn up
tightly as shown. Then grip the end A by the fingers of the left hand,
and let all the hitches drop off this hand. The end A will be pulled
through all the turns, and a knot will be formed in place of every hitch.
Fig. 3 shows three of the knots.

243

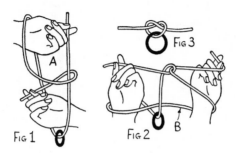

Fig 1   Fig 2   Fig 3

RING AND STRING KNOT

(1) Thread a ring on to a string and grasp the ends of the string by the right and left forefingers and thumbs, letting the loop of string hang down loosely in front of you, and with the ring in the centre.

(2) Pass the right hand above and to the back of the left hand, and lay the vertical string coming from the right hand across the back of the left wrist.

(3) Bring the right hand towards you and downwards, thus drawing its string down the inside of the left wrist.

(4) Draw the string in the right hand down diagonally to the right and pass the right hand to the right of and then behind the right vertical string, *i.e.*, the string coming from the fingers of the left hand.

(5) Then pass the right hand towards you through the hanging loop just above the ring. The string will now be as Fig. 1.

(6) Pass the right hand away from you through the space A and over the crossed strings and separate the hands horizontally, thus giving Fig. 2. All these movements should be done slowly.

(7) Turn the right hand palm outwards, which will bring the string B across the palm of this hand.

(8) Close the fingers of the right hand on the string B which crosses it ; grip this string and let the end of the string drop from your right finger and thumb. At the same time drop the loops off both hands when the ring will be finally knotted in the centre of the string. This latter movement should be done quickly.

244

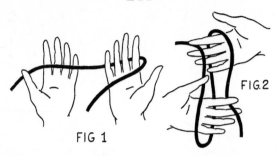

FIG 1   FIG. 2

BLOWING A KNOT ON A HANDKERCHIEF

Lay one end of the handkerchief across the palm of the left hand palm upwards, and grasp the other end of the handkerchief with the right hand palm downwards. Revolve the fingers of the right hand downwards, then towards you, and then away from you, thus bringing it palm upwards. The handkerchief will now cross the left palm, go behind the right fingers, and then to the left across the right palm, as in Fig. 1. Bring the hands into the position shown in Fig. 2, and grip the left end of the handkerchief between the first and second fingers of the right hand and the right end between the first and second fingers of the left hand. Release the grip of the thumbs and draw the hands apart, blow on the handkerchief, and the knot will suddenly appear. If done smartly and without hesitation this trick is most effective.

245

THE TALLOW CANDLES

Hold the left hand palm upwards, fingers pointing away from you, and pass it into the loop of string, letting the long loop hang down. With the right hand grasp the long loop and lift it up over the tips of the fingers of the left hand from the back, bringing one string between the first and second fingers of the left hand, and the other between the third and fourth fingers. Bring the left hand palm towards you, fingers pointing upwards, and pull the long loop down until the string is taut. Grip the string in the middle where it passes across the left palm, pull it out slightly and pass the loop over the tips of the second and third fingers. Pull the long loop until taut. Put the first finger of the right hand down from above into the loop on the palmar side of the left first finger, and the middle finger down into the loop on the little finger. Draw these loops out to the right as far as they will come. Then pass these four strings over the tips of the fingers of the left hand, bringing one string between the first and second finger, two strings between the second and third fingers, and one string between the third and fourth fingers, Fig. 1. Then

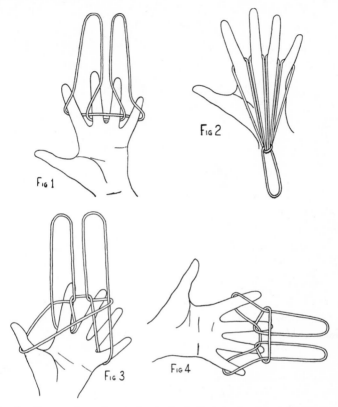

F_{IG} 1

F_{IG} 2

F_{IG} 3

F_{IG} 4

pass the four strings down through the loop of string which crosses the back of the second and third fingers, pulling them down until taut.

You are now ready to tell the story of " *the old man who stole a bunch of tallow candles.*" Lift the single string which goes across the back of the second and third fingers, over the tips of these fingers, and draw it gently to the right. This will form the bunch of tallow candles shown in Fig. 2. " *Here you see the tallow candles.*"

" *When the old man arrived home he hung the candles up on a nail.*" Here you hang the loop, without twisting it, on the left thumb.

" *The old man sat down in his high-backed chair and went to sleep.*"

With the first and second fingers of the right hand raise the loops from the back of the second and third fingers of the left hand, and at the same time bring the left hand downwards and palm upwards.

Spread the thumb out, thus forming the high-backed chair shown in Fig. 3.

" *When the old man woke up it was dark, so he got a pair of scissors and cut off one of the candles.*"

Here you drop the string off the thumb of the left hand and bring the strings horizontal, thus forming the pair of scissors shown in

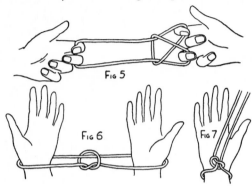

Fig. 4. The scissors can be opened and closed by separating the fingers.

" *Just then the Tipstaff came along carrying his staff with the King's crown on the top of it.*"

Here you drop the string from the fourth finger of your left hand and separate the hands until the string is taut, thus forming the staff shown in Fig. 5.

" *The Tipstaff arrested the old man and put the handcuffs on his wrists.*"

Here you drop the string from the third finger of your right hand and put your right wrist into the loop on your right first finger, making the handcuffs, Fig. 6.

" *The old man was taken to jail and hanged by the neck until he was dead.*"

Here you remove your left wrist from its loop and pull on the string straight, making Fig. 7.

246

ROPE ESCAPE

The old trick, " Cutting Through a Tree," described in " Winter Nights Entertainments," p. 97,* has been made into an excellent rope

---

* This volume has been republished by Dover Publications under the title "Easy-to-do Entertainments and Diversions with Coins, Cards, String, Paper and Matches."

escape by Fitzpatrick. It is done as follows. The accomplice to be roped stands with his face to the audience, and with the rope held horizontally across his back. His hands are clasped behind his back. (1) The right end of the rope is brought round to the front across his chest and to the left. The left end is brought round to the front, crossed over the right rope, and then to the right. *Note carefully* that the rope which starts originally on the right must always be laid next to the body, and that the left rope must cross above it. (2) The ropes are brought round and crossed at the back. (3) The ropes are crossed in front. (4) The person being roped clasps his hands and brings his two thumbs together and pointing horizontally towards his back. The left rope is now brought round to the back, looped round the thumbs, and back to the left again. The right rope is looped round the thumbs and brought back to the right in the same way. The right end is still nearest to the body if this, the key move, has been properly done. (5) The right rope is brought round in front, and then the left rope on the top of it. (6) The ropes are again crossed at the back ; and (7) crossed as before in front. If the loops are dropped off the thumbs the rope will come away when its ends are pulled apart.

247

STRING RELEASE

Hang a loop of string over your assistant's forefinger (held upright) and put your left thumb down into the other end of the loop, pulling the string taut and horizontal. With the middle finger of your right hand, pointing downwards, draw the left string above and across the right string. This should be done about one-third of the distance from you along the loop, and will put two crossings on the strings.

Then bring your right first finger down to the left of the strings and pass your left hand in a horizontal clockwise direction towards your assistant, keeping the strings taut and using your right fingers as a fulcrum. Place your left middle finger from above, down to the right of the strings, and, using it as a fulcrum, pass your right hand away from you anti-clockwise, and put the tip of your right middle finger on the tip of your assistant's upright forefinger.

Drop the strings from your right forefinger and your left middle finger, and pull on the loop round your left thumb. The string will now be released from your assistant's finger.

248

CUT AND RESTORED STRING

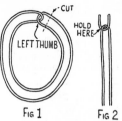

Fig 1   Fig 2

This trick is performed in many ways, but one of the oldest and simplest is as follows. Hold the ends of the loop by placing the fingers of each hand into it. Give the right hand end a complete twist through 360 degrees, and place this loop into your left hand, at the same time drawing the strings over your left palm until the crossing comes into and is covered by the left thumb (Fig. 1). Hold the strings by your right and left fingers and thumbs close to the crossing, and get someone to cut through both strings close to your left thumb. Let the two ends in your right hand drop, and it will look as if the string has been cut into two pieces as all the four ends can be seen (Fig. 2). Put the strings, which you are holding between your left finger and thumb, into your mouth and say you are going to join them together. Remove the short piece with your tongue. When you take the string out of your mouth you can show that the two ends have been restored.

GAMES WITH PAPER

"It is in good sooth a right pleasant and dainty pastime."

GAMES WITH PAPER

249
LETTER DISSECTION

Cut out the letter " E," and then cut it into eight pieces on the lines shown. Mix the pieces up and give them to someone to put together again. The solver should not be told what letter he has to make.

250
PAPER SQUARE

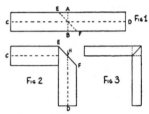

Take a long rectangle of paper (Fig. 1) and fold it along the line CD. Open the paper out and fold it on the line AB. Open out again and fold on the line EF. This brings the part HD at right angles to CH if care is taken to see that the point A is brought directly over CH and the point B over DH. This will give Fig. 2. Then fold on the line CH forwards, and on the line HD backwards. A little gum will hold all together.

251
MAKING A RIGHT ANGLE

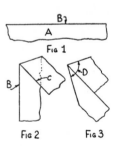

Take any piece of paper, one edge (B) of which must be straight. Fold one end down at about the angle shown in Fig. 2. Then fold B over to touch C, making Fig. 3. The angle D will be a right angle.

252
PAPER COMPASSES

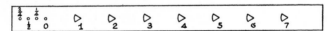

Take a strip of thick paper or cardboard and cut triangular holes 1 to 7. The points of the triangles should be 1 inch apart. Then, starting 1 inch away from 1, punch four small holes a ¼ of an inch apart. By putting a pin into one of the small holes and a pencil in one of the triangular holes, circles of all sizes, by ¼ inches, from 1 inch to 7¾ inches radius may be drawn.

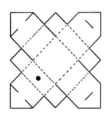

253
PAPER BOX

Take a square sheet of thick paper and fold on the dotted lines. Then cut as shown, and tuck the two points with side cuts into the points with central cuts, and a very strong box will be formed. If a hole is cut where the black dot is placed, smoke rings may be blown by filling the box with cigarette smoke and gently tapping the opposite side.

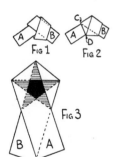

254
FIVE-POINTED STAR

Cut a narrow strip of thin paper and tie it into a thumb knot as in Fig. 1. Work the knot up gently and press it flat, thus making Fig. 2. Then fold A over on the line CD, thus making Fig. 3. If you hold the paper up to the light the five-pointed star will be clearly visible.

255
HEXAGON BOX

Take the outside case of a cigarette or match box and cut it into three equal pieces as shown. Place two of the pieces into the third, thus forming the box shown on the right.

256

TRUE LOVERS' KNOT

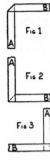

Take a long narrow strip of paper or a straw, and fold it across the middle as in Fig. 1. Next fold the end A upwards and press it down flat as in Fig. 2. Then fold B to the left, making Fig. 3. Keep on folding the ends alternately until the straw is exhausted. Then pull the ends out when a very pretty spiral cord will be formed. Twist the straw up as in Fig. 4, securing the crossing with a thread of cotton. These favours are worn by farm servants at the hiring fairs in Ireland, to show that they are open for engagement.

257

HEAD, BODY AND LEGS

This amusing game is played by three persons. Take a sheet of paper and fold it in three. The first player draws a head on the top third of the sheet, and then folds it back so that it cannot be seen. The second person draws a body and folds the paper back. The third person draws the legs. The first two artists should extend their drawings slightly on to the next portion, so that their successors will know where to join on their pictures.

258

CUTTING A SQUARE INTO FIVE SQUARES

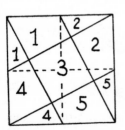

The illustration shows how this problem may be solved.

259

FOLDING AN EQUILATERAL TRIANGLE

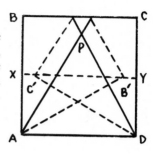

Fold a square of paper ABCD to give a crease joining X, the mid-point of AB, to Y, the mid-point of CD. Then make two folds, one with a crease through A which makes B come to a point B' which lies on XY, and another with a crease through D which makes C come to C', also on XY. The last two creases intersect in P, such that APD is an equilateral triangle.

260

PUZZLE TRIANGLE

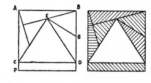

Lay out a triangle on a square of paper and cut along the full lines shown. Discard the triangular piece CDE and hand the remaining pieces to someone, asking him to lay them down on the table to form a triangle. The solution shown on the right is far from easy, as it seldom occurs to anyone to lay the pieces down to *enclose* a triangle.

261

FOLDING A BILLET DOUX

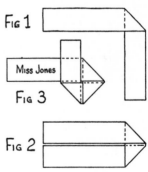

Fold the note up several times until it makes a narrow strip, and then fold the strip across at right angles as in Fig. 1. Fold one leg back, making Fig. 2. Next fold the same leg back and bring it to the front, thus locking the note up as in Fig. 3.

262

WIND WHEEL

Cut a circle of cardboard about 3 inches in diameter, and make sixteen cuts from the centre. Bend the points alternately backwards and forwards, as shown. The wind will bowl this disc at a great rate along a smooth pavement.

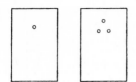

263

PINHOLE ILLUSION

Take two visiting cards and in one prick three small holes with the point of a pin. These holes should be very close together, as they must not cover an area greater than the pupil of the eye. In the other card prick a single hole as shown. Hold the card with three holes as close to your eye as possible, and hold the other card about 2 or 3 inches in front of the first. On looking at a light it will seem as if the far card has three holes also.

264

PIN UPSIDE DOWN

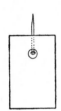

Prick a hole in a card about the size of the head of a pin. Hold the card about 3 inches away from your eye and hold a pin with its head upright close to your eye, With a little focussing and an adjustment of the distances the head of the pin will appear upside down.

265

CARD IN ENVELOPE

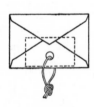

Secrete a visiting card in an envelope and show the apparently empty envelope and another similar card. Lay the second card down on the table. Punch a hole through the envelope as shown, and of course, through the card which is (unknown to your audience) inside. Pass a piece of string through the hole and tie the ends in a knot. Take up the card which lies on the table, place it in the envelope, and seal down. Cut the envelope along the bottom, pull on the string, when the card will come out threaded on to it. Get rid of the envelope and duplicate card as soon as possible.

266

TROUBLEWIT

This old paper game is not often seen now. Take a piece of heavy paper about 2 feet by 13 inches and draw parallel lines on it as in Fig. 1. These six lines should be 2 inches apart, starting from each edge, which will leave a centre space 1 inch wide. Fold on the two outside lines. Turn the paper over and fold on the next two lines. The paper looked at on edge will now be as in Fig. 2. Then, starting

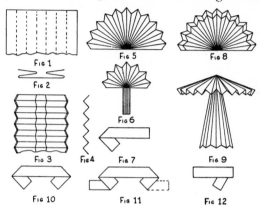

at the lower edge, fold the paper backwards and forwards in pleats about $\frac{3}{4}$ inch wide, thus making Fig. 3 and Fig. 4. The paper is now ready for forming into various interesting shapes, about 70 or 80 in all. First of all various fans, blinds, bonnets, etc., as Figs. 5 and 6 can be made from the paper in the form shown in Fig. 3. Then bend back one of the side folds as in Fig. 7, which will give another series of shapes. Fig. 8 is one made from the paper at this stage. The other side may now be unfolded, giving Fig. 10. Then the next two folds may be turned back as in Fig. 11. These unfoldings will give various new forms, one of which is shown in Fig. 9. Finally the second fold on each side may be closed up as in Fig. 12. This will give still another series.

267

CRYSTAL MODELS

METHOD OF MAKING

The following nets of crystals will enable anyone to build up solid models. The nets should be drawn on thin card, which is then cut half through on the various lines. The cards are then bent on these lines and the small marginal pieces shown dotted are fixed with glue.

268
PYRAMID

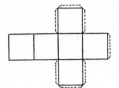

269
CUBE

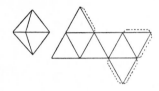

270
OCTAHEDRON

271
ICOSAHEDRON

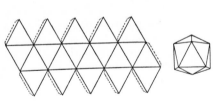

272
DODECAHEDRON

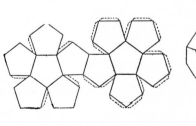

273

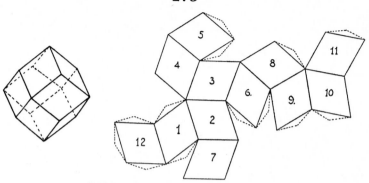

RHOMBIC DODECAHEDRON

274

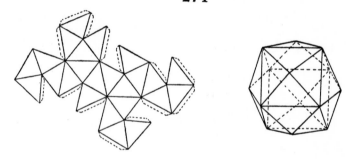

TETRAHEXAHEDRON

275

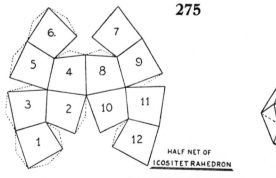

HALF NET OF
ICOSITETRAHEDRON

ICOSITETRAHEDRON

276

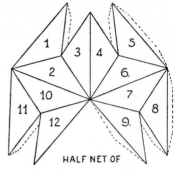

HALF NET OF
TRIAKISOCTAHEDRON

TRIAKISOCTAHEDRON

277
CUBE AND OCTAHEDRON

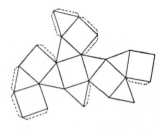

278
COPPER SULPHATE

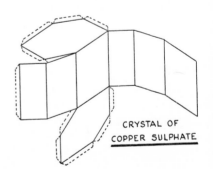

CRYSTAL OF
COPPER SULPHATE

MISCELLANEOUS

"The cause of the fountain is hidden, but the effect is very obvious."

MISCELLANEOUS

279
THE MAGNETIZED PENCIL

Hold your left hand palm upwards and
lay a pencil across it. Close your fist on the
pencil and grip your wrist with your right
hand. Turn your hand, palm downwards,
gradually open out your fingers, and then
bring your thumb slowly from underneath
the pencil. In spite of the fact that your
hand is fully opened, the pencil does not fall. Then close your fingers
again, turn your palm upwards, and open your fist. The secret of this
trick is, that when you turn your hand downwards, you support the
pencil against your palm with your right forefinger. If your right
fingers are kept close up to your sleeve, no one will notice that only
three fingers are showing above your wrist.

280
TELLING THE TIME BY THE POLE STAR

Imagine that the pole star is the centre of
a clock face and that the two pointer stars of
the Great Bear (the Plough) represent the hour
hand revolving round the centre, that six
o'clock on this dial is below the pole star, and twelve o'clock above it.
To find the actual time (correct to fifteen minutes), estimate the time
as shown by the pointers (six o'clock in the illustration), add to this
number the number of months and quarter month from the 1st of
January. Double the result, and subtract from $16\frac{1}{4}$, or if the result is
more than $16\frac{1}{4}$, then from $40\frac{1}{4}$. The result will be the number of hours
past twelve o'clock midday.

For example, if at the end of the first week in October the pointers
stand as in the illustration, *i.e.*, at six o'clock, then since it is $9\frac{1}{4}$ months
from the 1st of January, $9\frac{1}{4} + 6 = 15\frac{1}{4}$, and $15\frac{1}{4} \times 2 = 30\frac{1}{2}$. Then
$40\frac{1}{4}$ less $30\frac{1}{2} = 9\frac{3}{4}$. The actual time is therefore 9.45 p.m.

281

THREE-CARD TRICK

Cut a black face card diagonally and gum it to the face of a red card as shown. Take two other cards, throw all three on the table face downwards, and shuffle them about to show that there are only three cards. Pick up the double card and then the two others, placing them face upwards in your left hand. Fan the cards out, but be careful to keep the two indifferent cards together, so that they will appear as one card. Your audience will think they see three cards only, the Ten, King and Four. Turn your hand over, bringing the cards face downwards, and at the same time fan them out. If you ask someone to pick out the King he will, of course, take the centre card, which when turned up proves to be the Joker.

You can show the trick in many ways. For example, you can explain at length how the three-card men swindle their victims. When you fan out the cards face downwards, lay them on the table. Take up the two outside cards, placing the Four on the top of the false King. You can then show that your hand contains the Ten and Four, so obviously the King *must* be the one on the table. On turning it up it is, of course, the Joker.

282

TO FIND THE NUMBERS ON TWO DICE THROWN

Ask someone to throw a pair of dice and to choose one of them, to multiply this number by 5 and then add 7. Then ask him to multiply this result by 2 and to add the number on the second die. Then ask him what his total is. If you deduct 14 from this total you will have the two numbers originally thrown.

For example : say the 4 and 3 are thrown and that 4 is chosen.

Then $4 \times 5 = 20$ and $20 + 7 = 27$

$27 \times 2 = 54$ and $54 + 3 = 57$

Then $57 - 14 = 43$, which gives you the two numbers thrown, *i.e.*, 4 and 3.

283

TO FIND THE NUMBERS ON THREE DICE

Say the numbers thrown are *a*, *b* and *c*. Then work as follows :
First, $2a + 3$ multiply by 5.

Second, add 7 and add *b*.

Third, multiply by 2 and add 3.

Fourth, multiply by 5 and add *c*.

From the result of the above (which you must be told), subtract 235, and this will give you *a*, *b* and *c*.

284

TO FIND HOW MANY CARDS ARE LEFT

A takes any number of cards he chooses (about 10 to 15).

B is told to take twice as many as A has taken.

A is told to give six of his cards to B. (This is the key number, and should be altered each time the trick is shown.)

B gives A twice as many cards as A has in his hand.

You can now tell them that B has 18 cards in his hand. You arrive at this number by multiplying the key number by 3: in this case, $6 \times 3 = 18$. If A had been told to give say 5 of his cards to B, then B would be left finally with 15 cards.

285

TO GIVE THE RESULT OF A CALCULATION WITHOUT ASKING ANY QUESTIONS

Ask someone to think of a number, double it, add twelve, divide the result by four, and then to take *half the original number* from the result. The answer will be 3. This problem may be concisely stated thus :

Let *n* be the number thought of; then $\dfrac{2n + 12}{4} - \dfrac{n}{2} = 3$.

Other numbers may be given to alter the final result.

Thus $\dfrac{na + b}{c} - \dfrac{na}{c} = \dfrac{b}{c}$.

The simplest way to alter the result and the easiest to remember is to vary *b*, *i.e.*, the number to be added. Then the answer will be $\dfrac{b}{4}$.

For example, if 20 is added, the answer will be $20 \div 4 = 5$.

286

CURIOUS MULTIPLICATION

Multiply this number by any integer and all these figures will remain in the result. 52631578947368421o.

287

TO FIT LARGE CORK IN A SMALL BOTTLE

Cut the end of the cork as shown.

288

CROSSED OUT DIGIT

Write down a row of figures, say 129834, and add the digits = 27. Deduct 27 from the original row, thus :

$$129834$$
$$27$$
$$\overline{}$$
$$129807$$

Cross out any digit, say the 8, and add the remainder, which equals 19. If you are told the remainder, you can tell which digit was crossed out by deducting this remainder from the next multiple of 9, which in this case is 27. The crossed out digit 8 = 27 — 19. In this trick, however, when the crossed out digit is either 9 or 0 it is not possible to tell which has been crossed out, because in either case the sum of the digits is 9 or a multiple of 9.

289

BOOK TRICK

Ask someone to select a page of a book, to choose a word in any of the first nine lines, and in the first nine words of that line. He is then to multiply the number of the page by 2 and then by 5, to add 20, to add the number of the line, to add 5, to multiply by 10, to add the number of the word in the line, and to tell you the result of these operations. If you mentally deduct 250 from his result you can find the chosen word.

Example : Page 561, 9th line, 8th word.

Then $561 \times 10 = 5610 + 20 = 5630 + 9 = 5639 + 5 =$
$5644 \times 10 = 56440 + 8 = 56448.$

Then when you are told the number 56448 you deduct 250, which gives you 561,9,8.

290

STROBOSCOPIC DISC

The disc shown has 1, 2, 3, 4, 5, 6, 7 and 8 divisions, and if placed in the magic top described in " Winter Nights Entertainments," p. 135,* very pretty effects will be given under a neon light. For a gramophone speed disc working under the ordinary alternating current light, which has a periodicity of 50 per second, 75 divisions will show, when they look stationary, a speed of 80 per minute, or 77 divisions a speed of 78 per minute.

291

FOUR-EDGE BOOK

Many old books were treated in this way. Lay the book down on the table, push the top cover sideways as far as possible and clamp it firmly in a letterpress. A picture or any desired inscription is then drawn and painted on the sloping edge. When quite dry the book is unclamped and brought back to the normal shape. It is again clamped in the press with the edge square, and this edge is either painted red or gilt. This will render the picture invisible except when the leaves are bent back. A second picture may be painted by pushing the cover back in the opposite direction. Old books treated thus are much sought after at present.

292

SPECTRUM

Block up a window facing the sun, except for a small hole. A ray of sunlight will fall on the floor, and this ray will be visible owing to the dust in the atmosphere. Set a basin of water on the floor where the ray falls, and

---

* This volume has been republished by Dover Publications under the title "Easy-to-do Entertainments and Diversions with Coins, Cards, String, Paper and Matches."

hold the corner of a mirror in the water in such a position that it will catch the sunbeam and reflect it on to the wall or ceiling. A very beautiful spectrum of the primary colours will be the result, and brilliantly coloured flame effects may be obtained by slightly agitating the surface of the water.

293
TRANSMISSION OF SOUND

Tie the head of a poker in the middle of a piece of string. Let the poker hang down and press the two ends of the string in your ears. Strike the poker lightly with a piece of metal, when a loud booming will be heard. To others in the room the sound is scarcely audible.

294
SOUND ALONG A PLANK OF WOOD

Place your ear against the end of a long plank of timber, and get someone to lightly scratch the other end. The sound will be clearly transmitted to your ear. The ticking of a watch may also be clearly heard in this way.

295
MAGIC FIGURE

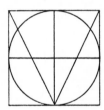

The adjacent diagram contains nearly all the usual geometrical figures. The alphabet and all the digits can also be traced out.

296

ARABIC NUMERALS

The arabic numerals are supposed to be formed as shown in the diagram.

297
OPTICAL ILLUSION

Is the upper figure smaller than the lower one ?

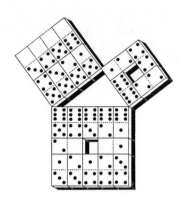

298
PYTHAGORAS IN DOMINOES

The illustration shows a right-angled triangle with sides of 3, 4 and 5, made up from dominoes having 9, 16 and 25 squares in the respective sides. The number of points on the large square is 75, which is equal to the sum of the points on the two smaller squares, *i.e.*, $27 + 48 = 75$.

299
TOWER OF CHECKERS

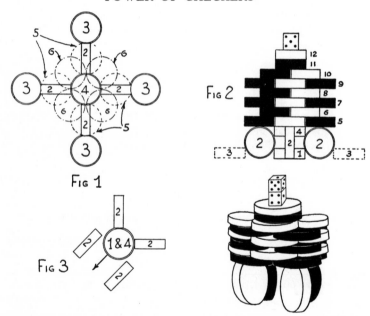

Place a checker (1) on the table, and set four checkers (2) up on edge round it. Place four checkers (3) up against (2) to hold them in place. Then carefully place (4) flat in the middle of (2). Then place four checkers (5) in a circle exactly over (2) and four checkers (6) in a circle on the top of (5) but in between them. Then four checkers (7)

directly over (5) and four checkers (8) directly over (6), and so on. The four checkers (3) may now be removed and added to the pile. Now comes the most difficult move. Turn two of the supporting checkers (2) on edge about a vertical axis, through an angle of 45 degrees, as shown in Fig. 3. This will allow (4) to drop down on (1). These two checkers (1 and 4) may now be pushed out with a pencil in the direction of the arrow, when they may be added to the pile. Finally the two checkers (2) can be turned back to their original positions and all the checkers will be supported quite securely on the edges of the four checkers (2).

300

BENHAM'S COLOUR TOP

Make a disc of cardboard about 5 inches in diameter, and mark it out with jet black ink as shown. Punch a hole in the centre and fit a peg into it so that the disc will spin. Spin the disc, when, although it only contains black and white, various complimentary colours will be seen. The effect is physiological.

301

London SW1

My dear Tipchin right. Please I hope that your let me maid has now hear if. You ceased to try are coming over to read the this week end contents of my and I will postcards. This send the car is written in the to the station way we arranged to meet and it looks as you. Best if it might do of all from the trick all yours ever
Peter.

SIMPLE POST-CARD CYPHER

Lady Tipchin was annoyed because her post-card messages aroused the curiosity of Glawdys Keyhole. So she devised a simple cypher which completely frustrated the knavish tricks of her simple handmaiden. She, for a week or so, got her correspondent to send her postcards on which were written nonsensical messages. Then when Glawdys had given the problem up as a bad job, her correspondent wrote her messages as shown. This is done by writing first down the left half of the card and then down the right side.

302
TANAGRAM

The illustration shows how the Chinese tanagram blocks should be cut. The original pieces were made from finely engraved mother-of-pearl or ivory about 2½ inches square. Black cardboard does quite well, and hundreds of amusing figures may be constructed with one or more sets of blocks.

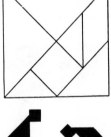

303
THE FOUR CUBES

This very ingenious puzzle was sold on the bookstalls in 1932. There are four coloured cubes, the lay-out of which is shown in the diagram. The puzzle is to arrange the four cubes in a row with the four colours showing on all four sides. The order of the colours does not matter.

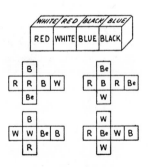

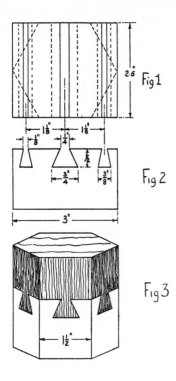

304

HEXAGON DOVETAIL

The drawing shows how this puzzle is constructed. Three dovetails are made in a pair of blocks 3″ × 2.6″. They are put together with glue and then the blocks are cut into a hexagon, as shown by the dotted lines in Fig. 1.

305

INTERLOCKED CARDS

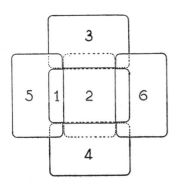

Lay the cards down on a table in the order shown by the numbers 1 to 4. Then tuck 5 and 6 under 1 and with their corners over 3 and 4. The cards will be interlocked and may be lifted by No. 2. By turning these six cards over and laying down on them another six cards, starting with a card in position 2, the twelve cards may be interlocked in a double layer.

306

THE TRIANGULAR DOVETAIL

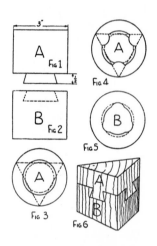

This puzzle dovetail is much easier to construct than the hexagon dovetail, and it is much more difficult to find out how it is made from an inspection of the finished article. To make the puzzle, two cylinders 3 inches in diameter should be turned in the lathe. These are preferably made of two different woods. An equilateral triangle is pencilled on the end of block A, as shown in Fig. 3, and a circle drawn just to overlap slightly the sides of the triangle. Another circle is drawn one-eighth of an inch larger in diameter. On this piece A turn a tapering spigot as shown in Fig. 1. It should be $\frac{1}{2}$ inch high and the same diameter as the larger circle, tapering down to the diameter of the smaller circle. A hollow of exactly the same shape is then turned in piece B, as shown by the dotted lines. Block A should now be cut on the lines into a triangle, and three small hollows should be cut out of the spigot, as shown in Fig. 4. Corresponding hollows should be cut in piece B, as shown in Fig. 5. If this has been accurately done, the spigot of A may be pushed down into the hollow of B, and a slight twist will cause the two blocks to interlock like a bayonet joint. The blocks can now be glued together. When all is dry, block B should be cut down into a triangular shape to correspond with block A. The finished puzzle is shown in Fig. 6.

307

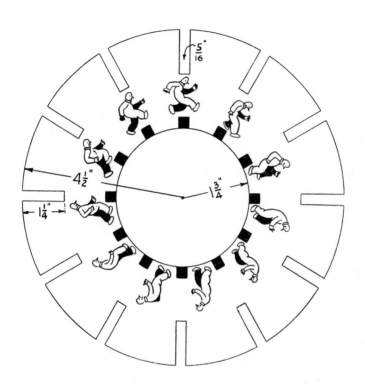

KINEMATOGRAPH DISC

Lay out a card about 9 inches in diameter, and cut twelve radial slots $1\frac{1}{4}$ by $\frac{5}{16}$ inch where shown. Draw eleven little men eccentric to the centre and with a progressive jumping action. Twelve squares should be made on the inner circle where shown. Punch a small hole in the centre, mount the card on a pin fixed in the end of a stick, and spin the card in front of a mirror. On looking through the slots at the reflection of the card in the mirror, the men will jump over the central squares. Many other designs may be drawn.

308

1	X	X	
2	X		X
4		X	X
8	X	X	
1 6	X	X	
3 2		X	X
6 4	X	X	X
1 2 8	X	125	X
2 5 6	219		
5 1 2			X
1 0 2 4			742
2 0 4 8			
4 0 9 6			
8 1 9 2			
1 6 3 8 4			
3 2 7 6 8			
6 5 5 3 6			
1 3 1 0 7 2			
2 6 2 1 4 4			
5 2 4 2 8 8			
1 0 4 8 5 7 6			

FINDING A NUMBER THOUGHT OF

This is a very ingenious method of finding a number thought of by merely asking questions, which are to be answered by " yes " or " no." First prepare a card as shown, which is arrived at by starting with 1, doubling it = 2, doubling again = 4, and so on. You then ask the person to think of a number and to divide it by 2. You ask him if there is any remainder. If he says yes, you place a X on the card opposite 1. Tell him to reject the remainder, and to divide his answer by 2. If he tells you that there is no remainder, you omit the X on your card. He is to keep on dividing by two until he gets down to 1, which, divided by 2 will leave a remainder of 1. If you then add all the numbers which are marked with a cross, the sum will give you the number he thought of. If, for example, the number thought of is 125. If this is divided by 2 there will be a remainder every time except the second. The crosses will therefore be opposite 1, 4, 8, 16, 32 and 64; which, when added together, equals 125.

309

MAGIC SQUARES

The writing of magic squares is a pastime which has interested mathematicians for hundreds of years. There are several well-known methods of constructing them, but up to the present no one has been able to prove the maximum number of possible arrangements with any given number of cells. Squares having an even number of cells are rather laborious and difficult to construct, but rules for writing squares having an odd number of cells are easy. A number of rules are given herewith which, once they are committed to memory, will make the writing of squares a very simple matter.

8	1	6
3	5	7
4	9	2

310

THIRD–ORDER SQUARE

There is only one square of this order. To make it, place 1 on the top centre square, then move up one square diagonally. As this carries you outside the boundary, place the number 2 in the corresponding cell at the bottom. Then move up diagonally again, and as this carries you outside the boundary on the right, place this number 3 in the corresponding cell on the left. Move up diagonally again, but as the required cell is already occupied by 1, move down vertically one cell and place the number 4 where shown ; 5 and 6 are placed by moving up one square diagonally. When you come to move up for number 7 you will be carried out beyond the boundary at the corner, but you cannot place 7 in the corresponding square in the other corner as it is occupied by 4, so you move down one as shown. The positions of 8 and 9 are found in the same way. If you think of these nine cells as being on the surface of a sphere, you will see that 1 is touching 9, 3 touching 7, 8 touching 2, and 6 touching 4. You have therefore only to write the numbers on this plan, i.e., by moving up diagonally one space except when the space is already occupied, when you must move down one space vertically.

311

MAGIC SQUARE TOTALS

The magic square, No. 310, will count 15 in all rows and columns and on the two diagonals. The general rule for any number of cells is as follows :

If n is the order of the square, the number to which it will count is given by :

$$\tfrac{1}{2}n(n^2 + 1).$$

In above nine-cell square which is of the third order, therefore :

$$\frac{3}{2}\left(9 + 1\right) = \frac{30}{2} = 15.$$

For a square of the fifth order, *i.e.*, 25 cells, we get $\dfrac{26 \times 5}{2} = 65.$

A seventh-order square therefore counts 175, and a ninth counts 369, and so on.

The squares count to the above numbers only when the starting figure is 1 and the numbers increase by 1.

Squares may also be written using odd or even numbers only, or the numbers may increase by any common difference, or in fact in any regular manner. It is also easy to write a square to count to any given number. The square on the right counts 16 in all the usual ways.

$8\frac{1}{3}$	$1\frac{1}{3}$	$6\frac{1}{3}$
$3\frac{1}{3}$	$5\frac{1}{3}$	$7\frac{1}{3}$
$4\frac{1}{3}$	$9\frac{1}{3}$	$2\frac{1}{3}$

11	4	9
6	8	10
7	12	5

312

THIRD-ORDER SQUARE TO COUNT 24

If it is desired to write a nine-cell square to count 24 (say), it can be done as follows :

Begin by placing 4 in the cell where 1 would normally come, and fill in the remainder by consecutive numbers. The square will count 24 instead of the usual 15. Suppose the given number is 125, then $\dfrac{125}{3} - 4 = 37\frac{2}{3}.$ This number is written in the cell normally occupied by 1, and the next number $38\frac{2}{3}$ will be in cell 2, $39\frac{2}{3}$ in cell 3 and so on. This square will be found to count to 125 in all the usual directions.

For a square of the fifth order, divide the given number by 5 and deduct 12 to arrive at the starting number.

The general rule for finding how much you must deduct to find the starting number is as follows : Divide the total count of the normal square by its order, and deduct 1.

For example, for a fifth-order square which as shown, normally counts 65.

Then $\dfrac{65}{5} - 1 = 12$, which is the number to be deducted as above.

For a seventh-order square the total is 175 ; then $\dfrac{175}{5} - 1 = 24.$

For ninth order : $\dfrac{369}{9} - 1 = 40$, and so on.

Say you are required to write a fifth-order square to count 135.
Then $\frac{135}{5} - 12 = 15$.

Therefore, starting with 15, then 16—17, and so on, the square will total 135.

313

FIFTH-ORDER MAGIC SQUARE

23	6	19	2	15
10	18	1	14	22
17	5	13	21	9
4	12	25	8	16
11	24	7	20	3

To write a simple square of 25 cells, which will count 65, start with 1 in any cell and fill in the cells by consecutive numbers, moving up one space diagonally. If the desired space is already filled, then move down three cells.

Any number which carries you outside the boundary must, of course, be placed in the corresponding cell on the opposite side.

314

SUPER MAGIC SQUARE

The last magic square is not very interesting, as it is not symmetrical, and only counts 65 in the rows, columns, and diagonals.

This illustration shows a much more perfect square. It is made by proceeding by knight's moves, *i.e.*, one up and one diagonally in the usual manner, and if at any move the square is already filled, then place the number in the next square below the previous number. On examining this square, it will be found that it can be counted up to 65 in a large additional number of ways. For example, any number added to its four surrounding numbers will equal 65. Say

23	6	19	2	15
4	12	25	8	16
10	18	1	14	22
11	24	7	20	3
17	5	13	21	9

1–25–14–7–18 or 12–6–25–18–4 = 65. Again any number and its four adjacent diagonal numbers will count 65. Say 12–23–19–1–10 = 65. Again the broken diagonals also count to 65. For example: 15–4–18–7–21 = 65, or 2–16–10–24–13 = 65, or 19–8–22–11–5 = 65. Again, as mentioned previously, as the square may be looked upon as a sphere, the adjacent numbers 10–4–18–11–22 = 65. It is an interesting exercise to determine the maximum number of ways in which it is possible to count 65.

315

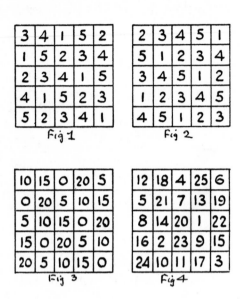

Fig 1

Fig 2

Fig 3

Fig 4

CONSTRUCTING FIFTH-ORDER SQUARES

A new method of constructing squares by Colonel Sankey yields an enormous number of different squares, and all similar in character to the above square. Proceed as follows:

Fig. 1 (1).—Set down a row of figures 1 to 5 in any order you please.

(2).—Write rows of figures 1 to 5 in the same order, but start with the middle figure of the previous row, and so on, until the 25 cells are completed.

Fig. 2.—(1) Write a row of figures 1 to 5 in any order you please.

(2) Write figures 1 to 5 in the same order, but start with the figure to the right of the middle of the previous row.

Fig. 3.—Re-write Fig. 1, but call 1 = 0, 2 = 5, 3 = 10, 4 = 15 and 5 = 20. This will give you Fig. 3.

Fig. 4.—Now re-write the square by adding together the numbers in the corresponding cells of Figs. 2 and 3. This gives the completed super magic square (Fig. 4).

35	23	18	13	1	45	40
4	48	36	31	26	21	9
22	17	12	7	44	39	34
47	42	30	25	20	8	3
16	11	6	43	38	33	28
41	29	24	19	14	2	46
10	5	49	37	32	27	15

316
SEVENTH-ORDER SYMMETRICAL SQUARE

This square of 49 numbers is written so that the mean number 25 is in the centre cell. The number 1 must be placed in the fifth cell of the first row, and then the square completed by knight's moves. These knight's moves are made upwards and to the right, and when the space is already filled, downwards and to the right. On analysing this square it will be seen that any group of six symmetrically placed cells and the centre cell 25 is magic. Also any related group of numbers counts to a constant number. For example : pairs—$35 + 15 = 50, 21 + 29 = 50, 43 + 7 = 50, 34 + 16 = 50$, and so on. Again four symmetrical numbers, say, $9-4-41-46 = 100$, any six numbers $= 150$, eight numbers $= 200$, and so on. There are therefore an enormous number of magic arrangements in any symmetrical square of this kind.

317

A symmetrical magic square of the eleventh order containing 121 numbers, may be written by placing the number 1 in the seventh cell of the first row, and completing by knight's moves as in No. 316.

318
SIMPLE MAGIC SQUARE

If you write down any square with consecutive numbers, say: —

$$\begin{array}{ccc} 1 & 2 & 3 \\ 4 & 5 & 6 \\ 7 & 8 & 9 \end{array}$$

You will find that all rows, or columns, or diagonals, which include the centre number, will count alike, *i.e.*, 3 times the centre number ; also the four corner numbers, 1—3—9—7, or the four central numbers 2—4—8—6, will be equal to 4 times the centre number. It will also be noticed that the two outer rows, or two outer columns, when added together, will equal 6 times the centre number. Similar results will be obtained if the rows increase consecutively and the columns vary by a common difference. All these relations apply to squares of any order.

43	23	36	19	32
21	29	45	25	33
27	35	18	31	42
28	44	24	37	20
34	22	30	41	26

319
MAGIC SQUARE TO COUNT TO ANY GIVEN NUMBER

Another method of writing this kind of square is (for a 25-cell square to count 153, say), to take the given number $\dfrac{153 - 60}{5} = 18$ and 3 over. Then start in any cell with the number 18, and fill in the cells by knight's moves in the usual way until you come to the twenty-first cell. To the number which would normally come in this cell, add 3, and then complete the other four cells in the usual way.

SOLUTIONS TO EASY PROBLEMS

1.—Daughter.

2.—12128 = £12 12s. 8d.

3.—£98,765 4s. 3½d. and £2,567 18s. 9¾d.

4.—Married the sister first; later married the woman who became his widow.

5.—good dog do a trick.

6.—The illustration shows the soldier's swagger cane and the dog's tail.

7.—Work it out for yourself.

8.—Smith, where Jones had had " *had had*," had had " *had.*" " *Had had*," had had the examiners' approval.

9.—Sniftkins was Silas's divorced wife.

10.—Sunday.

11.—15 miles.

12.—Because he must have been sleeping on duty.

13.—No one could know what the man was dreaming about.

14.—Bottle 2¼ cents; cork ¼ cent.

15.—Work it out for yourself.

16.—Aspired, Praised, Despair.

17.—Antidisestablishmentarianism.

18.—A quick brown fox jumps over the lazy dog.

19.—Fleas. A short poem on the same subject is " Adam-had'em."

20.—Too wise you are, too wise you be, I see you are too wise for me.

21.—$\left.\begin{array}{l} SIX - IX = S \\ IX - X = I \\ XL - L = X \end{array}\right\}$ SIX = 6.

22.—Six cats.

23.—Eight.

24.—The smith cut up one three-link piece, and with three welds joined up the remaining four pieces. His charge was therefore 6 cents.

25.—His mother.

26.—The same.

27.—With 5 couples there are 13 arrangements, with 6 couples 80, and with 10 couples there are 439,792.

28.—The weight rises at the same rate as the man.

29.—Nine trains.

30.—20 sacks.

31.—Three.

32.—Five dollars.

33.—About 3 feet.

34.—Four days out and four days back.

If n = the number of explorers, and d = the number of days' food carried by each one, then the greatest distance into the desert for one under the given conditions is $\dfrac{n \times d}{n + 1}$.

35.—Ginns had $15 and Itts had $24.

36.—YVAN. The names are Bar, Army, and Navy spelled backward.

37.—60 miles. He leaves at 9 a.m.

38.—Mary $94\frac{1}{4}$—Jane $74\frac{1}{4}$—Kate $41\frac{1}{4}$—Eliza $23\frac{1}{4}$.

39.—27 lbs.

40.—3 pigeons, 15 larks, 2 sparrows.

41.—

(1) Portions 1, 2, 3, 4 are the same shape and equal in area.

(2) Triangles 1 and 1, 2 and 2, 3 and 3, 4 and 4 are the four sons' portions.

42.—Ninety years.

43.—A blank note-book; about nothing.

44.—$9 - 6 = 3 \therefore IX - SIX = -S = 3$

$$3 + 7 = 10 \therefore -S + 7 = \begin{cases} -S \\ + \text{SEVEN} \\ = \overline{\text{EVEN}} = 10. \end{cases}$$

45.—(1) $\frac{1}{2}$—$1\frac{1}{2}$—$4\frac{1}{2}$—$13\frac{1}{2}$—$40\frac{1}{2}$.

(2) $13\frac{1}{2}$ in one pan; $4\frac{1}{2} + 1\frac{1}{2} + \frac{1}{2} = 6\frac{1}{2}$ lbs. together, with the article to be weighed in the other pan.

46.—

			8 gallon cask.	5 gallon measure.	3 gallon measure.
1	..	..	8	0	0
2	..	..	3	5	0
3	..	..	3	2	3
4	..	..	6	2	0
5	..	..	6	0	2
6	..	..	1	5	2
7	..	..	1	4	3
8	..	..	4	4	0

47.—First fill the 8-pint and from it fill the 7-pint. This will give 1 pint in the 8-pint measure. Then empty the 7-pint and pour into it the 1 pint from the 8-pint measure. Fill the 8-pint measure, and from it fill up the 7-pint. This will leave 2 pints in the 8-pint measure, and so on. Thus:—

7-pint.   0   7   0   1   1   7   0   2   2   7   and so on.
8-pint.   8   1   1   0   8   2   2   0   8   3

48.—There are many combinations which will satisfy this problem. Put 1 lump in cup number 1 ; 2 lumps in cup number 2, and 3 lumps in cup number 3. Then place cup number 3 into cup number 2. Each cup will now contain an odd number of lumps.

49.—The illustration shows one solution.

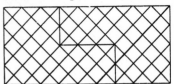

50.—(1) $123 + 4 - 5 + 67 - 89 = 100$

(2) $97 + \dfrac{8}{12} + \dfrac{4}{6} + \dfrac{5}{3} = 100$

(3) $123 - 45 - 67 + 89 = 100$

(4) $\dfrac{2}{3} + 1\dfrac{4}{8} + 97\dfrac{5}{6} = 100$

(5)
$$
\begin{array}{r}
15 \\
36 \\
47 \\
\hline
98 \\
2 \\
\hline
100
\end{array}
$$

(6) $91\dfrac{5742}{638}$

(7) $1 + 2 + 3 + 4 + 5 + 6 + 7 + (8 \times 9) = 100$

(8) $123 + 45 - 67 + 8 - 9 = 100$

51.—(1) $50 + 49 + \dfrac{38}{76} + \dfrac{1}{2} = 100$

(2) $98\dfrac{27}{54} + 1\dfrac{3}{6} + 0 = 100$

(3) $5\dfrac{3}{6} + 70 + 24\dfrac{9}{18} = 100$

(4) $19\dfrac{3}{6} + 80\dfrac{27}{54} = 100$

(5) $87 + 3\dfrac{12}{60} + 9\dfrac{4}{5} = 100$

52.—Feathers, because they are weighed by avoirdupois weight, and gold by troy weight.

53.—A gallon of whisky weighs more in winter than in summer. Once more, when would you buy ?

54.—Work this out with matches or coloured counters; seven crossings (three and a half round-trips) are required.

55.—E pushes B into C. E pushes A up, couples it to B, and draws A and B out into the right siding. E uncouples, goes up into C, and pushes A out on to the main line, leaving B in the right siding. E picks up A, and pushes it up into left siding, and then returns to the main line. Work the second part of this problem out for yourself.

56.—The illustration indicates how an ordinary cat may be made to look like a Manx. The 9.20 train would be just as effective.

57.—67½ lbs.

58.—Jones, 69 years 12 weeks ; Miss Jones, 30 years 40 weeks.

59.—18 years.

60.—FOREST—SOFTER—FOSTER.

61.—The friend who bought the ticket. He would have to pay another seven dollars to redeem the money order.

62.—$\dfrac{4}{.4} \times \dfrac{4}{.4} = 10 \times 10 = 100$

also—with four 9's : $99\dfrac{9}{9} = 100.$

63.—18 miles.

64.—The illustration shows two solutions.

65.—Two months longer.

66.—271 eggs.

SOLUTIONS TO NOT SO EASY PROBLEMS

67.—2.414 + miles.

68.—12,720 square feet (about).

69.—36 miles.

71.—D = 2.5199 feet.

72.—$34^3 - 33^3 = 16^3 - 9^3 = 15^3 - 2^3 = 3367$. (Solution by C.E.P.S.)

73.—$49\frac{1}{11}$ minutes past 3.

74.—Jane $16\frac{1}{2}$ years; Mary $27\frac{1}{2}$ years.

75.—$\frac{219}{3} = 73$; $\frac{438}{6} = 73$; $\frac{657}{9} = 73$.

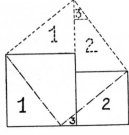

76.—The first piece was 119 × 119; the second piece was 120 × 120; the final square was 169 × 169. The illustration shows the simplest method of cutting up the squares, *i.e.*, place the two squares side by side, and cut on the chain-dotted lines. Then rearrange the pieces as shown by the dotted figures.

77.—14 and 20 years.

78.—An infinite number of times.

79.—$95 and $8.

80.—6¼ minutes.

81.—26 feet.

82.—41.62 feet.

83.— $\begin{cases} \text{Brown} & 21 \\ \text{Mary} & 71 \end{cases} \begin{cases} \text{Smith} & 49 \\ \text{Jane} & 169 \end{cases} \begin{cases} \text{Robinson} & 289 \\ \text{Eliza} & 1091 \end{cases}$ ∴ Eliza Robinson.

84.—11—12—13 and 14 inches. The total weight equals the weight of a ball with a 20-inch diameter.

85.—1—2—3—4 and 5 inches.

86.—2701—2702—2703.

87.—$\dfrac{567}{321489}$ and $\dfrac{854}{729316}$.

88.—20 per cent.

89.—7½ minutes.

90.—$\dfrac{240}{253}$.

91.—$\dfrac{123195}{215} = 573$.

92.—$\dfrac{19775}{35} = 565$.

93.—1st = B; 2nd = A; 3rd = C.

94.—1 = 4 gallons; 2 = 6½ gallons; 3 = 7½ gallons; 4 = 8 gallons; 5 = 9 gallons.

95.—Maximum box is 2 feet long by 1 foot broad, by 1 foot thick, which equals 2 cubic feet. A larger volume may be sent in a cylindrical parcel of 2 feet by 15¼ inches, which equals about 2.55 cubic feet.

96.—About 12 yards.

97.—The spider should walk from A to D across the carpet, and then from D to B along the baseboard. CD = 13.6 feet.

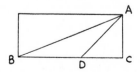

98.—100 feet.

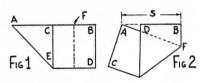

F₁G 1   F₁G 2

99.—Let AB $= x + y$ and AC $= x - y$. Then area of ABCD $= x^2 - y^2$ and AB $-$ AC $= 2y$.

First.—Fold AC up on the line AB as shown in Fig. 1. CB is therefore equal to $2y$.

Second.—Fold BD over to CE on line F and open out these folds. BF is therefore equal to y and AF $= x$.

Third.—Fold DB about the point F, so that ADB is a straight line. We now have the triangle AFB, and DBF is a right angle. As AF $= x$, BF $= y$, S is the side of a square which has an area equal to ABCD. (Solution by Major R. A. Bell.)

100.—18.2647 feet.

SOLUTIONS TO MATCH AND COIN PROBLEMS

101.—

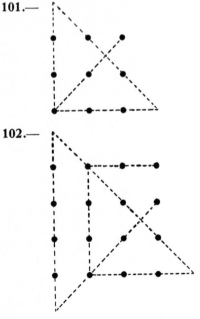

102.—

103.—   The method is similar to **102.**

105.—

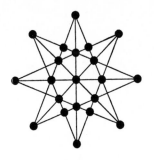

106.—

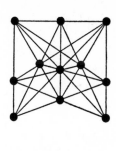

107.—

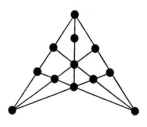

108.—

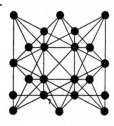

109.—

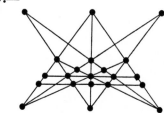

112.—The moves are as follows :

1st move 4 to touch 5 and 6
2nd ,, 5 ,, 1 ,, 2
3rd ,, 1 ,, 5 ,, 4

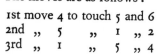

114.—The seven moves are (1 to 5), (3—7—1), (8—4—3—7), (6—2—8—4—3), (5—6—2—8), (1—5—6), (7—1).

116.—

117.—

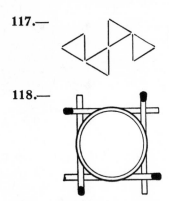

118.—

120.—Count always in the same direction, missing out one coin before starting the next count.

121.—You have only to add an odd number each time.

123.—Lift the top and bottom coin of the vertical arm and pile them on the centre coin. The cross will then count five in both directions.

124.—Put your 1st and 2nd fingers on 1 and 2, bring them round to the corresponding position on the right-hand side. Then push the six coins bodily to the left, leaving coins 1 and 2 in the position shown.

125.—This illustration shows how the coins are piled to satisfy the conditions laid down.

②	⑤	②		③	③	③		④	①	④
⑤		⑤		③		③		①		①
②	⑤	②		③	③	③		④	①	④
	28			*24*			*20*	

127.—Two.

128.—The play is as follows:

White { (1) Rook to Q6   (2) King to R7   (3) Rook to B6

Black { King to B square   King to B2

129.—The moves are as follows:

12—1—3—2—12—11—1—3—2—5—7—9—10—8—
6—4—5—7—9—10—8—6—4—5—7—9—10—8—6
—4—5—7—9—10—8—6—4—3—2—12—11—2—1
—2.

130.—The solution to this problem is the same as **114.**

131.—The 21 moves are:

2—4—6—5—3—1—2—4—6—5—3—1—2—4—6—
5—3—1—2—4—6.

132.—Add the three coins to the first four removed, which will leave seven in the second heap.

136.—Eighteen moves are:

(3—6) (10—1) (5—7) (6—2) (1—3) (7—9) (2—4)
(9—5) (4—10) (3—9) (8—4) (4—1) (9—6) (5—2)
(1—7) (6—3) (2—8) (7—5).

137.—The secret is this. You really take up two peas each time, and not one as stated, and when you are pretending to taste them, or it, rather, you place one in your mouth. The other one you place on your thumb to dry. You then pretend to take it up and put it in your ear, instead of which you open your thumb slightly and let it drop into your right hand to join the others. When you open your right hand you can show the correct number each time.

142.—This illustration shows how the men should be placed. It is easy to work out modifications of this problem.

144.—The number left in the upper row will be equal to the original difference plus the number which you asked him (say 4) to remove from the lower row.

147.—To do this, bring your lips down on to the end of the case at A and draw your breath in sharply. This will create a partial vacuum in the case and cause the tray to adhere to it. By holding the case with your finger and thumb and throwing your head backwards, the tray may be brought to the top and then laid down on the table in the position shown in Fig. **2.**

A CATALOG OF
SELECTED DOVER BOOKS
IN ALL FIELDS OF INTEREST

A CATALOG OF SELECTED DOVER BOOKS IN ALL FIELDS OF INTEREST

CONCERNING THE SPIRITUAL IN ART, Wassily Kandinsky. Pioneering work by father of abstract art. Thoughts on color theory, nature of art. Analysis of earlier masters. 12 illustrations. 80pp. of text. 5⅜ × 8½. 23411-8 Pa. $2.50

LEONARDO ON THE HUMAN BODY, Leonardo da Vinci. More than 1200 of Leonardo's anatomical drawings on 215 plates. Leonardo's text, which accompanies the drawings, has been translated into English. 506pp. 8⅜ × 11¾. 24483-0 Pa. $10.95

GOBLIN MARKET, Christina Rossetti. Best-known work by poet comparable to Emily Dickinson, Alfred Tennyson. With 46 delightfully grotesque illustrations by Laurence Housman. 64pp. 4 × 6¾. 24516-0 Pa. $2.50

THE HEART OF THOREAU'S JOURNALS, edited by Odell Shepard. Selections from *Journal*, ranging over full gamut of interests. 228pp. 5⅜ × 8½. 20741-2 Pa. $4.50

MR. LINCOLN'S CAMERA MAN: MATHEW B. BRADY, Roy Meredith. Over 300 Brady photos reproduced directly from original negatives, photos. Lively commentary. 368pp. 8⅜ × 11¼. 23021-X Pa. $11.95

PHOTOGRAPHIC VIEWS OF SHERMAN'S CAMPAIGN, George N. Barnard. Reprint of landmark 1866 volume with 61 plates: battlefield of New Hope Church, the Etawah Bridge, the capture of Atlanta, etc. 80pp. 9 × 12. 23445-2 Pa. $6.00

A SHORT HISTORY OF ANATOMY AND PHYSIOLOGY FROM THE GREEKS TO HARVEY, Dr. Charles Singer. Thoroughly engrossing non-technical survey. 270 illustrations. 211pp. 5⅜ × 8½. 20389-1 Pa. $4.50

REDOUTE ROSES IRON-ON TRANSFER PATTERNS, Barbara Christopher. Redouté was botanical painter to the Empress Josephine; transfer his famous roses onto fabric with these 24 transfer patterns. 80pp. 8¼ × 10⅞. 24292-7 Pa. $3.50

THE FIVE BOOKS OF ARCHITECTURE, Sebastiano Serlio. Architectural milestone, first (1611) English translation of Renaissance classic. Unabridged reproduction of original edition includes over 300 woodcut illustrations. 416pp. 9⅜ × 12¼. 24349-4 Pa. $14.95

CARLSON'S GUIDE TO LANDSCAPE PAINTING, John F. Carlson. Authoritative, comprehensive guide covers, every aspect of landscape painting. 34 reproductions of paintings by author; 58 explanatory diagrams. 144pp. 8⅜ × 11. 22927-0 Pa. $4.95

101 PUZZLES IN THOUGHT AND LOGIC, C.R. Wylie, Jr. Solve murders, robberies, see which fishermen are liars—purely by reasoning! 107pp. 5⅜ × 8½. 20367-0 Pa. $2.00

TEST YOUR LOGIC, George J. Summers. 50 more truly new puzzles with new turns of thought, new subtleties of inference. 100pp. 5⅜ × 8½. 22877-0 Pa. $2.25

THE MURDER BOOK OF J.G. REEDER, Edgar Wallace. Eight suspenseful stories by bestselling mystery writer of 20s and 30s. Features the donnish Mr. J.G. Reeder of Public Prosecutor's Office. 128pp. 5⅜ × 8½. (Available in U.S. only)
24374-5 Pa. $3.50

ANNE ORR'S CHARTED DESIGNS, Anne Orr. Best designs by premier needlework designer, all on charts: flowers, borders, birds, children, alphabets, etc. Over 100 charts, 10 in color. Total of 40pp. 8¼ × 11.
23704-4 Pa. $2.25

BASIC CONSTRUCTION TECHNIQUES FOR HOUSES AND SMALL BUILDINGS SIMPLY EXPLAINED, U.S. Bureau of Naval Personnel. Grading, masonry, woodworking, floor and wall framing, roof framing, plastering, tile setting, much more. Over 675 illustrations. 568pp. 6½ × 9¼.
20242-9 Pa. $8.95

MATISSE LINE DRAWINGS AND PRINTS, Henri Matisse. Representative collection of female nudes, faces, still lifes, experimental works, etc., from 1898 to 1948. 50 illustrations. 48pp. 8⅜ × 11¼.
23877-6 Pa. $2.50

HOW TO PLAY THE CHESS OPENINGS, Eugene Znosko-Borovsky. Clear, profound examinations of just what each opening is intended to do and how opponent can counter. Many sample games. 147pp. 5⅜ × 8½.
22795-2 Pa. $2.95

DUPLICATE BRIDGE, Alfred Sheinwold. Clear, thorough, easily followed account: rules, etiquette, scoring, strategy, bidding; Goren's point-count system, Blackwood and Gerber conventions, etc. 158pp. 5⅜ × 8½.
22741-3 Pa. $3.00

SARGENT PORTRAIT DRAWINGS, J.S. Sargent. Collection of 42 portraits reveals technical skill and intuitive eye of noted American portrait painter, John Singer Sargent. 48pp. 8¼ × 11⅛.
24524-1 Pa. $2.95

ENTERTAINING SCIENCE EXPERIMENTS WITH EVERYDAY OBJECTS, Martin Gardner. Over 100 experiments for youngsters. Will amuse, astonish, teach, and entertain. Over 100 illustrations. 127pp. 5⅜ × 8½.
24201-3 Pa. $2.50

TEDDY BEAR PAPER DOLLS IN FULL COLOR: A Family of Four Bears and Their Costumes, Crystal Collins. A family of four Teddy Bear paper dolls and nearly 60 cut-out costumes. Full color, printed one side only. 32pp. 9¼ × 12¼.
24550-0 Pa. $3.50

NEW CALLIGRAPHIC ORNAMENTS AND FLOURISHES, Arthur Baker. Unusual, multi-useable material: arrows, pointing hands, brackets and frames, ovals, swirls, birds, etc. Nearly 700 illustrations. 80pp. 8⅜ × 11¼.
24095-9 Pa. $3.75

DINOSAUR DIORAMAS TO CUT & ASSEMBLE, M. Kalmenoff. Two complete three-dimensional scenes in full color, with 31 cut-out animals and plants. Excellent educational toy for youngsters. Instructions; 2 assembly diagrams. 32pp. 9¼ × 12¼.
24541-1 Pa. $3.95

SILHOUETTES: A PICTORIAL ARCHIVE OF VARIED ILLUSTRATIONS, edited by Carol Belanger Grafton. Over 600 silhouettes from the 18th to 20th centuries. Profiles and full figures of men, women, children, birds, animals, groups and scenes, nature, ships, an alphabet. 144pp. 8⅜ × 11¼.
23781-8 Pa. $4.95

25 KITES THAT FLY, Leslie Hunt. Full, easy-to-follow instructions for kites made from inexpensive materials. Many novelties. 70 illustrations. 110pp. 5⅜ × 8½.
22550-X Pa. $2.25

PIANO TUNING, J. Cree Fischer. Clearest, best book for beginner, amateur. Simple repairs, raising dropped notes, tuning by easy method of flattened fifths. No previous skills needed. 4 illustrations. 201pp. 5⅜ × 8½.   23267-0 Pa. $3.50

EARLY AMERICAN IRON-ON TRANSFER PATTERNS, edited by Rita Weiss. 75 designs, borders, alphabets, from traditional American sources. 48pp. 8¼ × 11.
23162-3 Pa. $1.95

CROCHETING EDGINGS, edited by Rita Weiss. Over 100 of the best designs for these lovely trims for a host of household items. Complete instructions, illustrations. 48pp. 8¼ × 11.   24031-2 Pa. $2.25

FINGER PLAYS FOR NURSERY AND KINDERGARTEN, Emilie Poulsson. 18 finger plays with music (voice and piano); entertaining, instructive. Counting, nature lore, etc. Victorian classic. 53 illustrations. 80pp. 6½ × 9¼. 22588-7 Pa. $1.95

BOSTON THEN AND NOW, Peter Vanderwarker. Here in 59 side-by-side views are photographic documentations of the city's past and present. 119 photographs. Full captions. 122pp. 8¼ × 11.   24312-5 Pa. $6.95

CROCHETING BEDSPREADS, edited by Rita Weiss. 22 patterns, originally published in three instruction books 1939-41. 39 photos, 8 charts. Instructions. 48pp. 8¼ × 11.   23610-2 Pa. $2.00

HAWTHORNE ON PAINTING, Charles W. Hawthorne. Collected from notes taken by students at famous Cape Cod School; hundreds of direct, personal *apercus*, ideas, suggestions. 91pp. 5⅜ × 8½.   20653-X Pa. $2.50

THERMODYNAMICS, Enrico Fermi. A classic of modern science. Clear, organized treatment of systems, first and second laws, entropy, thermodynamic potentials, etc. Calculus required. 160pp. 5⅜ × 8½.   60361-X Pa. $4.00

TEN BOOKS ON ARCHITECTURE, Vitruvius. The most important book ever written on architecture. Early Roman aesthetics, technology, classical orders, site selection, all other aspects. Morgan translation. 331pp. 5⅜ × 8½. 20645-9 Pa. $5.50

THE CORNELL BREAD BOOK, Clive M. McCay and Jeanette B. McCay. Famed high-protein recipe incorporated into breads, rolls, buns, coffee cakes, pizza, pie crusts, more. Nearly 50 illustrations. 48pp. 8¼ × 11.   23995-0 Pa. $2.00

THE CRAFTSMAN'S HANDBOOK, Cennino Cennini. 15th-century handbook, school of Giotto, explains applying gold, silver leaf; gesso; fresco painting, grinding pigments, etc. 142pp. 6⅛ × 9¼.   20054-X Pa. $3.50

FRANK LLOYD WRIGHT'S FALLINGWATER, Donald Hoffmann. Full story of Wright's masterwork at Bear Run, Pa. 100 photographs of site, construction, and details of completed structure. 112pp. 9¼ × 10.   23671-4 Pa. $6.50

OVAL STAINED GLASS PATTERN BOOK, C. Eaton. 60 new designs framed in shape of an oval. Greater complexity, challenge with sinuous cats, birds, mandalas framed in antique shape. 64pp. 8¼ × 11.   24519-5 Pa. $3.50

THE BOOK OF WOOD CARVING, Charles Marshall Sayers. Still finest book for beginning student. Fundamentals, technique; gives 34 designs, over 34 projects for panels, bookends, mirrors, etc. 33 photos. 118pp. 7¾ × 10⅝. 23654-4 Pa. $3.95

CARVING COUNTRY CHARACTERS, Bill Higginbotham. Expert advice for beginning, advanced carvers on materials, techniques for creating 18 projects—mirthful panorama of American characters. 105 illustrations. 80pp. 8⅜ × 11. 24135-1 Pa. $2.50

300 ART NOUVEAU DESIGNS AND MOTIFS IN FULL COLOR, C.B. Grafton. 44 full-page plates display swirling lines and muted colors typical of Art Nouveau. Borders, frames, panels, cartouches, dingbats, etc. 48pp. 9⅜ × 12¼. 24354-0 Pa. $6.00

SELF-WORKING CARD TRICKS, Karl Fulves. Editor of *Pallbearer* offers 72 tricks that work automatically through nature of card deck. No sleight of hand needed. Often spectacular. 42 illustrations. 113pp. 5⅜ × 8½. 23334-0 Pa. $3.50

CUT AND ASSEMBLE A WESTERN FRONTIER TOWN, Edmund V. Gillon, Jr. Ten authentic full-color buildings on heavy cardboard stock in H-O scale. Sheriff's Office and Jail, Saloon, Wells Fargo, Opera House, others. 48pp. 9¼ × 12¼. 23736-2 Pa. $3.95

CUT AND ASSEMBLE AN EARLY NEW ENGLAND VILLAGE, Edmund V. Gillon, Jr. Printed in full color on heavy cardboard stock. 12 authentic buildings in H-O scale: Adams home in Quincy, Mass., Oliver Wight house in Sturbridge, smithy, store, church, others. 48pp. 9¼ × 12¼. 23536-X Pa. $3.95

THE TALE OF TWO BAD MICE, Beatrix Potter. Tom Thumb and Hunca Munca squeeze out of their hole and go exploring. 27 full-color Potter illustrations. 59pp. 4¼ × 5½. (Available in U.S. only) 23065-1 Pa. $1.50

CARVING FIGURE CARICATURES IN THE OZARK STYLE, Harold L. Enlow. Instructions and illustrations for ten delightful projects, plus general carving instructions. 22 drawings and 47 photographs altogether. 39pp. 8⅜ × 11. 23151-8 Pa. $2.50

A TREASURY OF FLOWER DESIGNS FOR ARTISTS, EMBROIDERERS AND CRAFTSMEN, Susan Gaber. 100 garden favorites lushly rendered by artist for artists, craftsmen, needleworkers. Many form frames, borders. 80pp. 8¼ × 11. 24096-7 Pa. $3.50

CUT & ASSEMBLE A TOY THEATER/THE NUTCRACKER BALLET, Tom Tierney. Model of a complete, full-color production of Tchaikovsky's classic. 6 backdrops, dozens of characters, familiar dance sequences. 32pp. 9⅜ × 12¼. 24194-7 Pa. $4.50

ANIMALS: 1,419 COPYRIGHT-FREE ILLUSTRATIONS OF MAMMALS, BIRDS, FISH, INSECTS, ETC., edited by Jim Harter. Clear wood engravings present, in extremely lifelike poses, over 1,000 species of animals. 284pp. 9 × 12. 23766-4 Pa. $9.95

MORE HAND SHADOWS, Henry Bursill. For those at their 'finger ends," 16 more effects—Shakespeare, a hare, a squirrel, Mr. Punch, and twelve more—each explained by a full-page illustration. Considerable period charm. 30pp. 6½ × 9¼. 21384-6 Pa. $1.95

SURREAL STICKERS AND UNREAL STAMPS, William Rowe. 224 haunting, hilarious stamps on gummed, perforated stock, with images of elephants, geisha girls, George Washington, etc. 16pp. one side. 8¼ × 11.   24371-0 Pa. $3.50

GOURMET KITCHEN LABELS, Ed Sibbett, Jr. 112 full-color labels (4 copies each of 28 designs). Fruit, bread, other culinary motifs. Gummed and perforated. 16pp. 8¼ × 11.   24087-8 Pa. $2.95

PATTERNS AND INSTRUCTIONS FOR CARVING AUTHENTIC BIRDS, H.D. Green. Detailed instructions, 27 diagrams, 85 photographs for carving 15 species of birds so life-like, they'll seem ready to fly! 8¼ × 11.   24222-6 Pa. $2.75

FLATLAND, E.A. Abbott. Science-fiction classic explores life of 2-D being in 3-D world. 16 illustrations. 103pp. 5⅜ × 8.   20001-9 Pa. $2.00

DRIED FLOWERS, Sarah Whitlock and Martha Rankin. Concise, clear, practical guide to dehydration, glycerinizing, pressing plant material, and more. Covers use of silica gel. 12 drawings. 32pp. 5⅜ × 8½.   21802-3 Pa. $1.00

EASY-TO-MAKE CANDLES, Gary V. Guy. Learn how easy it is to make all kinds of decorative candles. Step-by-step instructions. 82 illustrations. 48pp. 8¼ × 11.
     23881-4 Pa. $2.50

SUPER STICKERS FOR KIDS, Carolyn Bracken. 128 gummed and perforated full-color stickers: GIRL WANTED, KEEP OUT, BORED OF EDUCATION, X-RATED, COMBAT ZONE, many others. 16pp. 8¼ × 11.   24092-4 Pa. $2.50

CUT AND COLOR PAPER MASKS, Michael Grater. Clowns, animals, funny faces...simply color them in, cut them out, and put them together, and you have 9 paper masks to play with and enjoy. 32pp. 8¼ × 11.   23171-2 Pa. $2.25

A CHRISTMAS CAROL: THE ORIGINAL MANUSCRIPT, Charles Dickens. Clear facsimile of Dickens manuscript, on facing pages with final printed text. 8 illustrations by John Leech, 4 in color on covers. 144pp. 8⅜ × 11¼.
     20980-6 Pa. $5.95

CARVING SHOREBIRDS, Harry V. Shourds & Anthony Hillman. 16 full-size patterns (all double-page spreads) for 19 North American shorebirds with step-by-step instructions. 72pp. 9¼ × 12¼.   24287-0 Pa. $4.95

THE GENTLE ART OF MATHEMATICS, Dan Pedoe. Mathematical games, probability, the question of infinity, topology, how the laws of algebra work, problems of irrational numbers, and more. 42 figures. 143pp. 5⅜ × 8½. (EBE)
     22949-1 Pa. $3.50

READY-TO-USE DOLLHOUSE WALLPAPER, Katzenbach & Warren, Inc. Stripe, 2 floral stripes, 2 allover florals, polka dot; all in full color. 4 sheets (350 sq. in.) of each, enough for average room. 48pp. 8¼ × 11.   23495-9 Pa. $2.95

MINIATURE IRON-ON TRANSFER PATTERNS FOR DOLLHOUSES, DOLLS, AND SMALL PROJECTS, Rita Weiss and Frank Fontana. Over 100 miniature patterns: rugs, bedspreads, quilts, chair seats, etc. In standard dollhouse size. 48pp. 8¼ × 11.   23741-9 Pa. $1.95

THE DINOSAUR COLORING BOOK, Anthony Rao. 45 renderings of dinosaurs, fossil birds, turtles, other creatures of Mesozoic Era. Scientifically accurate. Captions. 48pp. 8¼ × 11.   24022-3 Pa. $2.25

JAPANESE DESIGN MOTIFS, Matsuya Co. Mon, or heraldic designs. Over 4000 typical, beautiful designs: birds, animals, flowers, swords, fans, geometrics; all beautifully stylized. 213pp. 11⅜ × 8¼. 22874-6 Pa. $7.95

THE TALE OF BENJAMIN BUNNY, Beatrix Potter. Peter Rabbit's cousin coaxes him back into Mr. McGregor's garden for a whole new set of adventures. All 27 full-color illustrations. 59pp. 4¼ × 5½. (Available in U.S. only) 21102-9 Pa. $1.50

THE TALE OF PETER RABBIT AND OTHER FAVORITE STORIES BOXED SET, Beatrix Potter. Seven of Beatrix Potter's best-loved tales including Peter Rabbit in a specially designed, durable boxed set. 4¼ × 5½. Total of 447pp. 158 color illustrations. (Available in U.S. only) 23903-9 Pa. $10.80

PRACTICAL MENTAL MAGIC, Theodore Annemann. Nearly 200 astonishing feats of mental magic revealed in step-by-step detail. Complete advice on staging, patter, etc. Illustrated. 320pp. 5⅜ × 8½. 24426-1 Pa. $5.95

CELEBRATED CASES OF JUDGE DEE (DEE GOONG AN), translated by Robert Van Gulik. Authentic 18th-century Chinese detective novel; Dee and associates solve three interlocked cases. Led to van Gulik's own stories with same characters. Extensive introduction. 9 illustrations. 237pp. 5⅜ × 8½.
23337-5 Pa. $4.50

CUT & FOLD EXTRATERRESTRIAL INVADERS THAT FLY, M. Grater. Stage your own lilliputian space battles.By following the step-by-step instructions and explanatory diagrams you can launch 22 full-color fliers into space. 36pp. 8¼ × 11. 24478-4 Pa. $2.95

CUT & ASSEMBLE VICTORIAN HOUSES, Edmund V. Gillon, Jr. Printed in full color on heavy cardboard stock, 4 authentic Victorian houses in H-O scale: Italian-style Villa, Octagon, Second Empire, Stick Style. 48pp. 9¼ × 12¼.
23849-0 Pa. $3.95

BEST SCIENCE FICTION STORIES OF H.G. WELLS, H.G. Wells. Full novel *The Invisible Man*, plus 17 short stories: "The Crystal Egg," "Aepyornis Island," "The Strange Orchid," etc. 303pp. 5⅜ × 8½. (Available in U.S. only)
21531-8 Pa. $4.95

TRADEMARK DESIGNS OF THE WORLD, Yusaku Kamekura. A lavish collection of nearly 700 trademarks, the work of Wright, Loewy, Klee, Binder, hundreds of others. 160pp. 8¾ × 8. (Available in U.S. only) 24191-2 Pa. $5.00

THE ARTIST'S AND CRAFTSMAN'S GUIDE TO REDUCING, ENLARGING AND TRANSFERRING DESIGNS, Rita Weiss. Discover, reduce, enlarge, transfer designs from any objects to any craft project. 12pp. plus 16 sheets special graph paper. 8¼ × 11. 24142-4 Pa. $3.25

TREASURY OF JAPANESE DESIGNS AND MOTIFS FOR ARTISTS AND CRAFTSMEN, edited by Carol Belanger Grafton. Indispensable collection of 360 traditional Japanese designs and motifs redrawn in clean, crisp black-and-white, copyright-free illustrations. 96pp. 8¼ × 11. 24435-0 Pa. $3.95

CHANCERY CURSIVE STROKE BY STROKE, Arthur Baker. Instructions and illustrations for each stroke of each letter (upper and lower case) and numerals. 54 full-page plates. 64pp. 8¼ × 11. 24278-1 Pa. $2.50

THE ENJOYMENT AND USE OF COLOR, Walter Sargent. Color relationships, values, intensities; complementary colors, illumination, similar topics. Color in nature and art. 7 color plates, 29 illustrations. 274pp. 5⅜ × 8½. 20944-X Pa. $4.50

SCULPTURE PRINCIPLES AND PRACTICE, Louis Slobodkin. Step-by-step approach to clay, plaster, metals, stone; classical and modern. 253 drawings, photos. 255pp. 8⅛ × 11. 22960-2 Pa. $7.50

VICTORIAN FASHION PAPER DOLLS FROM HARPER'S BAZAR, 1867-1898, Theodore Menten. Four female dolls with 28 elegant high fashion costumes, printed in full color. 32pp. 9¼ × 12¼. 23453-3 Pa. $3.50

FLOPSY, MOPSY AND COTTONTAIL: A Little Book of Paper Dolls in Full Color, Susan LaBelle. Three dolls and 21 costumes (7 for each doll) show Peter Rabbit's siblings dressed for holidays, gardening, hiking, etc. Charming borders, captions. 48pp. 4¼ × 5½. 24376-1 Pa. $2.25

NATIONAL LEAGUE BASEBALL CARD CLASSICS, Bert Randolph Sugar. 83 big-leaguers from 1909-69 on facsimile cards. Hubbell, Dean, Spahn, Brock plus advertising, info, no duplications. Perforated, detachable. 16pp. 8¼ × 11. 24308-7 Pa. $2.95

THE LOGICAL APPROACH TO CHESS, Dr. Max Euwe, et al. First-rate text of comprehensive strategy, tactics, theory for the amateur. No gambits to memorize, just a clear, logical approach. 224pp. 5⅜ × 8½. 24353-2 Pa. $4.50

MAGICK IN THEORY AND PRACTICE, Aleister Crowley. The summation of the thought and practice of the century's most famous necromancer, long hard to find. Crowley's best book. 436pp. 5⅜ × 8½. (Available in U.S. only) 23295-6 Pa. $6.50

THE HAUNTED HOTEL, Wilkie Collins. Collins' last great tale; doom and destiny in a Venetian palace. Praised by T.S. Eliot. 127pp. 5⅜ × 8½. 24333-8 Pa. $3.00

ART DECO DISPLAY ALPHABETS, Dan X. Solo. Wide variety of bold yet elegant lettering in handsome Art Deco styles. 100 complete fonts, with numerals, punctuation, more. 104pp. 8⅛ × 11. 24372-9 Pa. $4.00

CALLIGRAPHIC ALPHABETS, Arthur Baker. Nearly 150 complete alphabets by outstanding contemporary. Stimulating ideas; useful source for unique effects. 154 plates. 157pp. 8⅜ × 11¼. 21045-6 Pa. $4.95

ARTHUR BAKER'S HISTORIC CALLIGRAPHIC ALPHABETS, Arthur Baker. From monumental capitals of first-century Rome to humanistic cursive of 16th century, 33 alphabets in fresh interpretations. 88 plates. 96pp. 9 × 12. 24054-1 Pa. $4.50

LETTIE LANE PAPER DOLLS, Sheila Young. Genteel turn-of-the-century family very popular then and now. 24 paper dolls. 16 plates in full color. 32pp. 9¼ × 12¼. 24089-4 Pa. $3.50

CATALOG OF DOVER BOOKS

KEYBOARD WORKS FOR SOLO INSTRUMENTS, G.F. Handel. 35 neglected works from Handel's vast oeuvre, originally jotted down as improvisations. Includes Eight Great Suites, others. New sequence. 174pp. 9⅜ × 12¼.
24338-9 Pa. $7.50

AMERICAN LEAGUE BASEBALL CARD CLASSICS, Bert Randolph Sugar. 82 stars from 1900s to 60s on facsimile cards. Ruth, Cobb, Mantle, Williams, plus advertising, info, no duplications. Perforated, detachable. 16pp. 8¼ × 11.
24286-2 Pa. $2.95

A TREASURY OF CHARTED DESIGNS FOR NEEDLEWORKERS, Georgia Gorham and Jeanne Warth. 141 charted designs: owl, cat with yarn, tulips, piano, spinning wheel, covered bridge, Victorian house and many others. 48pp. 8¼ × 11.
23558-0 Pa. $1.95

DANISH FLORAL CHARTED DESIGNS, Gerda Bengtsson. Exquisite collection of over 40 different florals: anemone, Iceland poppy, wild fruit, pansies, many others. 45 illustrations. 48pp. 8¼ × 11.
23957-8 Pa. $1.75

OLD PHILADELPHIA IN EARLY PHOTOGRAPHS 1839-1914, Robert F. Looney. 215 photographs: panoramas, street scenes, landmarks, President-elect Lincoln's visit, 1876 Centennial Exposition, much more. 230pp. 8⅜ × 11¾.
23345-6 Pa. $9.95

PRELUDE TO MATHEMATICS, W.W. Sawyer. Noted mathematician's lively, stimulating account of non-Euclidean geometry, matrices, determinants, group theory, other topics. Emphasis on novel, striking aspects. 224pp. 5⅜ × 8½.
24401-6 Pa. $4.50

ADVENTURES WITH A MICROSCOPE, Richard Headstrom. 59 adventures with clothing fibers, protozoa, ferns and lichens, roots and leaves, much more. 142 illustrations. 232pp. 5⅜ × 8½.
23471-1 Pa. $3.95

IDENTIFYING ANIMAL TRACKS: MAMMALS, BIRDS, AND OTHER ANIMALS OF THE EASTERN UNITED STATES, Richard Headstrom. For hunters, naturalists, scouts, nature-lovers. Diagrams of tracks, tips on identification. 128pp. 5⅜ × 8.
24442-3 Pa. $3.50

VICTORIAN FASHIONS AND COSTUMES FROM HARPER'S BAZAR, 1867-1898, edited by Stella Blum. Day costumes, evening wear, sports clothes, shoes, hats, other accessories in over 1,000 detailed engravings. 320pp. 9⅜ × 12¼.
22990-4 Pa. $9.95

EVERYDAY FASHIONS OF THE TWENTIES AS PICTURED IN SEARS AND OTHER CATALOGS, edited by Stella Blum. Actual dress of the Roaring Twenties, with text by Stella Blum. Over 750 illustrations, captions. 156pp. 9 × 12.
24134-3 Pa. $8.50

HALL OF FAME BASEBALL CARDS, edited by Bert Randolph Sugar. Cy Young, Ted Williams, Lou Gehrig, and many other Hall of Fame greats on 92 full-color, detachable reprints of early baseball cards. No duplication of cards with *Classic Baseball Cards*. 16pp. 8¼ × 11.
23624-2 Pa. $3.50

THE ART OF HAND LETTERING, Helm Wotzkow. Course in hand lettering, Roman, Gothic, Italic, Block, Script. Tools, proportions, optical aspects, individual variation. Very quality conscious. Hundreds of specimens. 320pp. 5⅜ × 8½.
21797-3 Pa. $4.95

HOW THE OTHER HALF LIVES, Jacob A. Riis. Journalistic record of filth, degradation, upward drive in New York immigrant slums, shops, around 1900. New edition includes 100 original Riis photos, monuments of early photography. 233pp. 10 × 7⅞. 22012-5 Pa. $7.95

CHINA AND ITS PEOPLE IN EARLY PHOTOGRAPHS, John Thomson. In 200 black-and-white photographs of exceptional quality photographic pioneer Thomson captures the mountains, dwellings, monuments and people of 19th-century China. 272pp. 9⅜ × 12¼. 24393-1 Pa. $12.95

GODEY COSTUME PLATES IN COLOR FOR DECOUPAGE AND FRAMING, edited by Eleanor Hasbrouk Rawlings. 24 full-color engravings depicting 19th-century Parisian haute couture. Printed on one side only. 56pp. 8¼ × 11.
23879-2 Pa. $3.95

ART NOUVEAU STAINED GLASS PATTERN BOOK, Ed Sibbett, Jr. 104 projects using well-known themes of Art Nouveau: swirling forms, florals, peacocks, and sensuous women. 60pp. 8¼ × 11. 23577-7 Pa. $3.50

QUICK AND EASY PATCHWORK ON THE SEWING MACHINE: Susan Aylsworth Murwin and Suzzy Payne. Instructions, diagrams show exactly how to machine sew 12 quilts. 48pp. of templates. 50 figures. 80pp. 8¼ × 11.
23770-2 Pa. $3.50

THE STANDARD BOOK OF QUILT MAKING AND COLLECTING, Marguerite Ickis. Full information, full-sized patterns for making 46 traditional quilts, also 150 other patterns. 483 illustrations. 273pp. 6⅞ × 9⅝. 20582-7 Pa. $5.95

LETTERING AND ALPHABETS, J. Albert Cavanagh. 85 complete alphabets lettered in various styles; instructions for spacing, roughs, brushwork. 121pp. 8¾ × 8. 20053-1 Pa. $3.75

LETTER FORMS: 110 COMPLETE ALPHABETS, Frederick Lambert. 110 sets of capital letters; 16 lower case alphabets; 70 sets of numbers and other symbols. 110pp. 8⅛ × 11. 22872-X Pa. $4.50

ORCHIDS AS HOUSE PLANTS, Rebecca Tyson Northen. Grow cattleyas and many other kinds of orchids—in a window, in a case, or under artificial light. 63 illustrations. 148pp. 5⅜ × 8½. 23261-1 Pa. $2.95

THE MUSHROOM HANDBOOK, Louis C.C. Krieger. Still the best popular handbook. Full descriptions of 259 species, extremely thorough text, poisons, folklore, etc. 32 color plates; 126 other illustrations. 560pp. 5⅜ × 8½.
21861-9 Pa. $8.50

THE DORÉ BIBLE ILLUSTRATIONS, Gustave Doré. All wonderful, detailed plates: Adam and Eve, Flood, Babylon, life of Jesus, etc. Brief King James text with each plate. 241 plates. 241pp. 9 × 12. 23004-X Pa. $8.95

THE BOOK OF KELLS: Selected Plates in Full Color, edited by Blanche Cirker. 32 full-page plates from greatest manuscript-icon of early Middle Ages. Fantastic, mysterious. Publisher's Note. Captions. 32pp. 9⅜ × 12¼. 24345-1 Pa. $4.50

THE PERFECT WAGNERITE, George Bernard Shaw. Brilliant criticism of the Ring Cycle, with provocative interpretation of politics, economic theories behind the Ring. 136pp. 5⅜ × 8½. (Available in U.S. only) 21707-8 Pa. $3.00

THE RIME OF THE ANCIENT MARINER, Gustave Doré, S.T. Coleridge. Doré's finest work, 34 plates capture moods, subtleties of poem. Full text. 77pp. 9¼ × 12.   22305-1 Pa. $4.95

SONGS OF INNOCENCE, William Blake. The first and most popular of Blake's famous "Illuminated Books," in a facsimile edition reproducing all 31 brightly colored plates. Additional printed text of each poem. 64pp. 5¼ × 7.
22764-2 Pa. $3.00

AN INTRODUCTION TO INFORMATION THEORY, J.R. Pierce. Second (1980) edition of most impressive non-technical account available. Encoding, entropy, noisy channel, related areas, etc. 320pp. 5⅜ × 8½.   24061-4 Pa. $4.95

THE DIVINE PROPORTION: A STUDY IN MATHEMATICAL BEAUTY, H.E. Huntley. "Divine proportion" or "golden ratio" in poetry, Pascal's triangle, philosophy, psychology, music, mathematical figures, etc. Excellent bridge between science and art. 58 figures. 185pp. 5⅜ × 8½.   22254-3 Pa. $3.95

THE DOVER NEW YORK WALKING GUIDE: From the Battery to Wall Street, Mary J. Shapiro. Superb inexpensive guide to historic buildings and locales in lower Manhattan: Trinity Church, Bowling Green, more. Complete Text; maps. 36 illustrations. 48pp. 3⅞ × 9¼.   24225-0 Pa. $2.50

NEW YORK THEN AND NOW, Edward B. Watson, Edmund V. Gillon, Jr. 83 important Manhattan sites: on facing pages early photographs (1875-1925) and 1976 photos by Gillon. 172 illustrations. 171pp. 9¼ × 10.   23361-8 Pa. $7.95

HISTORIC COSTUME IN PICTURES, Braun & Schneider. Over 1450 costumed figures from dawn of civilization to end of 19th century. English captions. 125 plates. 256pp. 8⅜ × 11¼.   23150-X Pa. $7.50

VICTORIAN AND EDWARDIAN FASHION: A Photographic Survey, Alison Gernsheim. First fashion history completely illustrated by contemporary photographs. Full text plus 235 photos, 1840-1914, in which many celebrities appear. 240pp. 6½ × 9¼.   24205-6 Pa. $6.00

CHARTED CHRISTMAS DESIGNS FOR COUNTED CROSS-STITCH AND OTHER NEEDLECRAFTS, Lindberg Press. Charted designs for 45 beautiful needlecraft projects with many yuletide and wintertime motifs. 48pp. 8¼ × 11.
24356-7 Pa. $1.95

101 FOLK DESIGNS FOR COUNTED CROSS-STITCH AND OTHER NEEDLE-CRAFTS, Carter Houck. 101 authentic charted folk designs in a wide array of lovely representations with many suggestions for effective use. 48pp. 8¼ × 11.
24369-9 Pa. $2.25

FIVE ACRES AND INDEPENDENCE, Maurice G. Kains. Great back-to-the-land classic explains basics of self-sufficient farming. The one book to get. 95 illustrations. 397pp. 5⅜ × 8½.   20974-1 Pa. $4.95

A MODERN HERBAL, Margaret Grieve. Much the fullest, most exact, most useful compilation of herbal material. Gigantic alphabetical encyclopedia, from aconite to zedoary, gives botanical information, medical properties, folklore, economic uses, and much else. Indispensable to serious reader. 161 illustrations. 888pp. 6½ × 9¼. (Available in U.S. only)   22798-7, 22799-5 Pa., Two-vol. set $16.45

CATALOG OF DOVER BOOKS

DECORATIVE NAPKIN FOLDING FOR BEGINNERS, Lillian Oppenheimer and Natalie Epstein. 22 different napkin folds in the shape of a heart, clown's hat, love knot, etc. 63 drawings. 48pp. 8¼ × 11. 23797-4 Pa. $1.95

DECORATIVE LABELS FOR HOME CANNING, PRESERVING, AND OTHER HOUSEHOLD AND GIFT USES, Theodore Menten. 128 gummed, perforated labels, beautifully printed in 2 colors. 12 versions. Adhere to metal, glass, wood, ceramics. 24pp. 8¼ × 11. 23219-0 Pa. $2.95

EARLY AMERICAN STENCILS ON WALLS AND FURNITURE, Janet Waring. Thorough coverage of 19th-century folk art: techniques, artifacts, surviving specimens. 166 illustrations, 7 in color. 147pp. of text. 7⅞ × 10¾. 21906-2 Pa. $9.95

AMERICAN ANTIQUE WEATHERVANES, A.B. & W.T. Westervelt. Extensively illustrated 1883 catalog exhibiting over 550 copper weathervanes and finials. Excellent primary source by one of the principal manufacturers. 104pp. 6⅛ × 9¼. 24396-6 Pa. $3.95

ART STUDENTS' ANATOMY, Edmond J. Farris. Long favorite in art schools. Basic elements, common positions, actions. Full text, 158 illustrations. 159pp. 5⅜ × 8½. 20744-7 Pa. $3.95

BRIDGMAN'S LIFE DRAWING, George B. Bridgman. More than 500 drawings and text teach you to abstract the body into its major masses. Also specific areas of anatomy. 192pp. 6½ × 9¼. (EA) 22710-3 Pa. $4.50

COMPLETE PRELUDES AND ETUDES FOR SOLO PIANO, Frederic Chopin. All 26 Preludes, all 27 Etudes by greatest composer of piano music. Authoritative Paderewski edition. 224pp. 9 × 12. (Available in U.S. only) 24052-5 Pa. $7.50

PIANO MUSIC 1888-1905, Claude Debussy. Deux Arabesques, Suite Bergamesque, Masques, 1st series of Images, etc. 9 others, in corrected editions. 175pp. 9⅜ × 12¼. (ECE) 22771-5 Pa. $5.95

TEDDY BEAR IRON-ON TRANSFER PATTERNS, Ted Menten. 80 iron-on transfer patterns of male and female Teddys in a wide variety of activities, poses, sizes. 48pp. 8¼ × 11. 24596-9 Pa. $2.25

A PICTURE HISTORY OF THE BROOKLYN BRIDGE, M.J. Shapiro. Profusely illustrated account of greatest engineering achievement of 19th century. 167 rare photos & engravings recall construction, human drama. Extensive, detailed text. 122pp. 8¼ × 11. 24403-2 Pa. $7.95

NEW YORK IN THE THIRTIES, Berenice Abbott. Noted photographer's fascinating study shows new buildings that have become famous and old sights that have disappeared forever. 97 photographs. 97pp. 11⅜ × 10. 22967-X Pa. $6.50

MATHEMATICAL TABLES AND FORMULAS, Robert D. Carmichael and Edwin R. Smith. Logarithms, sines, tangents, trig functions, powers, roots, reciprocals, exponential and hyperbolic functions, formulas and theorems. 269pp. 5⅜ × 8½. 60111-0 Pa. $3.75

HANDBOOK OF MATHEMATICAL FUNCTIONS WITH FORMULAS, GRAPHS, AND MATHEMATICAL TABLES, edited by Milton Abramowitz and Irene A. Stegun. Vast compendium: 29 sets of tables, some to as high as 20 places. 1,046pp. 8 × 10½. 61272-4 Pa. $19.95

REASON IN ART, George Santayana. Renowned philosopher's provocative, seminal treatment of basis of art in instinct and experience. Volume Four of *The Life of Reason*. 230pp. 5⅜ × 8. 24358-3 Pa. $4.50

LANGUAGE, TRUTH AND LOGIC, Alfred J. Ayer. Famous, clear introduction to Vienna, Cambridge schools of Logical Positivism. Role of philosophy, elimination of metaphysics, nature of analysis, etc. 160pp. 5⅜ × 8½. (USCO) 20010-8 Pa. $2.75

BASIC ELECTRONICS, U.S. Bureau of Naval Personnel. Electron tubes, circuits, antennas, AM, FM, and CW transmission and receiving, etc. 560 illustrations. 567pp. 6½ × 9¼. 21076-6 Pa. $8.95

THE ART DECO STYLE, edited by Theodore Menten. Furniture, jewelry, metalwork, ceramics, fabrics, lighting fixtures, interior decors, exteriors, graphics from pure French sources. Over 400 photographs. 183pp. 8⅜ × 11¼. 22824-X Pa. $6.95

THE FOUR BOOKS OF ARCHITECTURE, Andrea Palladio. 16th-century classic covers classical architectural remains, Renaissance revivals, classical orders, etc. 1738 Ware English edition. 216 plates. 110pp. of text. 9½ × 12¾. 21308-0 Pa. $11.50

THE WIT AND HUMOR OF OSCAR WILDE, edited by Alvin Redman. More than 1000 ripostes, paradoxes, wisecracks: Work is the curse of the drinking classes, I can resist everything except temptations, etc. 258pp. 5⅜ × 8½. (USCO) 20602-5 Pa. $3.50

THE DEVIL'S DICTIONARY, Ambrose Bierce. Barbed, bitter, brilliant witticisms in the form of a dictionary. Best, most ferocious satire America has produced. 145pp. 5⅜ × 8½. 20487-1 Pa. $2.50

ERTÉ'S FASHION DESIGNS, Erté. 210 black-and-white inventions from *Harper's Bazar*, 1918-32, plus 8pp. full-color covers. Captions. 88pp. 9 × 12. 24203-X Pa. $6.50

ERTÉ GRAPHICS, Erté. Collection of striking color graphics: *Seasons, Alphabet, Numerals, Aces* and *Precious Stones*. 50 plates, including 4 on covers. 48pp. 9⅜ × 12¼. 23580-7 Pa. $6.95

PAPER FOLDING FOR BEGINNERS, William D. Murray and Francis J. Rigney. Clearest book for making origami sail boats, roosters, frogs that move legs, etc. 40 projects. More than 275 illustrations. 94pp. 5⅜ × 8½. 20713-7 Pa. $2.25

ORIGAMI FOR THE ENTHUSIAST, John Montroll. Fish, ostrich, peacock, squirrel, rhinoceros, Pegasus, 19 other intricate subjects. Instructions. Diagrams. 128pp. 9 × 12. 23799-0 Pa. $4.95

CROCHETING NOVELTY POT HOLDERS, edited by Linda Macho. 64 useful, whimsical pot holders feature kitchen themes, animals, flowers, other novelties. Surprisingly easy to crochet. Complete instructions. 48pp. 8¼ × 11. 24296-X Pa. $1.95

CROCHETING DOILIES, edited by Rita Weiss. Irish Crochet, Jewel, Star Wheel, Vanity Fair and more. Also luncheon and console sets, runners and centerpieces. 51 illustrations. 48pp. 8¼ × 11. 23424-X Pa. $2.00

YUCATAN BEFORE AND AFTER THE CONQUEST, Diego de Landa. Only significant account of Yucatan written in the early post-Conquest era. Translated by William Gates. Over 120 illustrations. 162pp. 5⅜ × 8½.   23622-6 Pa. $3.50

ORNATE PICTORIAL CALLIGRAPHY, E.A. Lupfer. Complete instructions, over 150 examples help you create magnificent "flourishes" from which beautiful animals and objects gracefully emerge. 8⅛ × 11.   21957-7 Pa. $2.95

DOLLY DINGLE PAPER DOLLS, Grace Drayton. Cute chubby children by same artist who did Campbell Kids. Rare plates from 1910s. 30 paper dolls and over 100 outfits reproduced in full color. 32pp. 9¼ × 12¼.   23711-7 Pa. $3.50

CURIOUS GEORGE PAPER DOLLS IN FULL COLOR, H. A. Rey, Kathy Allert. Naughty little monkey-hero of children's books in two doll figures, plus 48 full-color costumes: pirate, Indian chief, fireman, more. 32pp. 9¼ × 12¼.
24386-9 Pa. $3.50

GERMAN: HOW TO SPEAK AND WRITE IT, Joseph Rosenberg. Like *French, How to Speak and Write It.* Very rich modern course, with a wealth of pictorial material. 330 illustrations. 384pp. 5⅜ × 8½. (USUKO)   20271-2 Pa. $4.75

CATS AND KITTENS: 24 Ready-to-Mail Color Photo Postcards, D. Holby. Handsome collection; feline in a variety of adorable poses. Identifications. 12pp. on postcard stock. 8¼ × 11.   24469-5 Pa. $2.95

MARILYN MONROE PAPER DOLLS, Tom Tierney. 31 full-color designs on heavy stock, from *The Asphalt Jungle, Gentlemen Prefer Blondes,* 22 others. 1 doll. 16 plates. 32pp. 9⅜ × 12¼.   23769-9 Pa. $3.50

FUNDAMENTALS OF LAYOUT, F.H. Wills. All phases of layout design discussed and illustrated in 121 illustrations. Indispensable as student's text or handbook for professional. 124pp. 8⅜.× 11.   21279-3 Pa. $4.50

FANTASTIC SUPER STICKERS, Ed Sibbett, Jr. 75 colorful pressure-sensitive stickers. Peel off and place for a touch of pizzazz: clowns, penguins, teddy bears, etc. Full color. 16pp. 8¼ × 11.   24471-7 Pa. $2.95

LABELS FOR ALL OCCASIONS, Ed Sibbett, Jr. 6 labels each of 16 different designs—baroque, art nouveau, art deco, Pennsylvania Dutch, etc.—in full color. 24pp. 8¼ × 11.   23688-9 Pa. $2.95

HOW TO CALCULATE QUICKLY: RAPID METHODS IN BASIC MATHE-MATICS, Henry Sticker. Addition, subtraction, multiplication, division, checks, etc. More than 8000 problems, solutions. 185pp. 5 × 7¼.   20295-X Pa. $2.95

THE CAT COLORING BOOK, Karen Baldauski. Handsome, realistic renderings of 40 splendid felines, from American shorthair to exotic types. 44 plates. Captions. 48pp. 8¼ × 11.   24011-8 Pa. $2.25

THE TALE OF PETER RABBIT, Beatrix Potter. The inimitable Peter's terrifying adventure in Mr. McGregor's garden, with all 27 wonderful, full-color Potter illustrations. 55pp. 4¼ × 5½. (Available in U.S. only)   22827-4 Pa. $1.60

BASIC ELECTRICITY, U.S. Bureau of Naval Personnel. Batteries, circuits, conductors, AC and DC, inductance and capacitance, generators, motors, trans-formers, amplifiers, etc. 349 illustrations. 448pp. 6½ × 9¼.   20973-3 Pa. $7.95

CATALOG OF DOVER BOOKS

SOURCE BOOK OF MEDICAL HISTORY, edited by Logan Clendening, M.D. Original accounts ranging from Ancient Egypt and Greece to discovery of X-rays: Galen, Pasteur, Lavoisier, Harvey, Parkinson, others. 685pp. 5⅜ × 8½.
20621-1 Pa. $10.95

THE ROSE AND THE KEY, J.S. Lefanu. Superb mystery novel from Irish master. Dark doings among an ancient and aristocratic English family. Well-drawn characters; capital suspense. Introduction by N. Donaldson. 448pp. 5⅜ × 8½.
24377-X Pa. $6.95

SOUTH WIND, Norman Douglas. Witty, elegant novel of ideas set on languorous Mediterranean island of Nepenthe. Elegant prose, glittering epigrams, mordant satire. 1917 masterpiece. 416pp. 5⅜ × 8½. (Available in U.S. only)
24361-3 Pa. $5.95

RUSSELL'S CIVIL WAR PHOTOGRAPHS, Capt. A.J. Russell. 116 rare Civil War Photos: Bull Run, Virginia campaigns, bridges, railroads, Richmond, Lincoln's funeral car. Many never seen before. Captions. 128pp. 9⅜ × 12¼.
24283-8 Pa. $6.95

PHOTOGRAPHS BY MAN RAY: 105 Works, 1920-1934. Nudes, still lifes, landscapes, women's faces, celebrity portraits (Dali, Matisse, Picasso, others), rayographs. Reprinted from rare gravure edition. 128pp. 9⅜ × 12¼. (Available in U.S. only)
23842-3 Pa. $6.95

STAR NAMES: THEIR LORE AND MEANING, Richard H. Allen. Star names, the zodiac, constellations: folklore and literature associated with heavens. The basic book of its field, fascinating reading. 563pp. 5⅜ × 8½.
21079-0 Pa. $7.95

BURNHAM'S CELESTIAL HANDBOOK, Robert Burnham, Jr. Thorough guide to the stars beyond our solar system. Exhaustive treatment. Alphabetical by constellation: Andromeda to Cetus in Vol. 1; Chamaeleon to Orion in Vol. 2; and Pavo to Vulpecula in Vol. 3. Hundreds of illustrations. Index in Vol. 3. 2000pp. 6⅛ × 9¼.
23567-X, 23568-8, 23673-0 Pa. Three-vol. set $36.85

THE ART NOUVEAU STYLE BOOK OF ALPHONSE MUCHA, Alphonse Mucha. All 72 plates from *Documents Decoratifs* in original color. Stunning, essential work of Art Nouveau. 80pp. 9⅜ × 12¼.
24044-4 Pa. $7.95

DESIGNS BY ERTE; FASHION DRAWINGS AND ILLUSTRATIONS FROM "HARPER'S BAZAR," Erte. 310 fabulous line drawings and 14 *Harper's Bazar* covers, 8 in full color. Erte's exotic temptresses with tassels, fur muffs, long trains, coifs, more. 129pp. 9⅜ × 12¼.
23397-9 Pa. $6.95

HISTORY OF STRENGTH OF MATERIALS, Stephen P. Timoshenko. Excellent historical survey of the strength of materials with many references to the theories of elasticity and structure. 245 figures. 452pp. 5⅜ × 8½. 61187-6 Pa. $8.95

Prices subject to change without notice.
Available at your book dealer or write for free catalog to Dept. GI, Dover Publications, Inc., 31 East 2nd St. Mineola, N.Y. 11501. Dover publishes more than 175 books each year on science, elementary and advanced mathematics, biology, music, art, literary history, social sciences and other areas.